D1209986

CITY OF THE BEES

FRANK S. STUART

City of the Bees

WHITTLESEY HOUSE

McGraw-Hill Book Company, Inc · New York

CITY OF THE BEES

All rights reserved. This book, or parts thereof, may not be reproduced in any form without permission of the publisher.

Copyright, 1947, 1949, *by* FRANK S. STUART

SECOND PRINTING

PUBLISHED BY WHITTLESEY HOUSE

A DIVISION OF THE McGRAW-HILL BOOK COMPANY, INC.

PRINTED IN THE UNITED STATES OF AMERICA

595.7
St9c
QL
565
.S15

1 4 5 1 8 7

F-72399

$3.75 - $2.50

McClurg

8-14-51

46672

For Deirdre

Preface

THOUGH I deplore Prefaces, it may prevent misunderstanding to say briefly that this book is an imaginative fantasy.

I could lead you to the hillside and take you through the wood to the oak tree. Bee colonies really do establish themselves in trees. Badgers attack them, and so do hordes of robber bees. Diseases decimate them. Ants steal honey from bees' tongues. Wasps paralyze bees, and store the living, helpless victims in wasp larders.

High romance always deals with realities. The events recorded here really do happen to bees and birds and animals, in the same world where, so pitifully unheeding, "civilized" man stamps and frets along his little rut into his grave, never looking round at the beauty, savagery, emotion, and wonder that he rushes blindly past.

FRANK S. STUART

Contents

CHAPTER ONE

Gold-dust Ballerina

INTO *the air!* The bee shot up into the glowing sky, unable to beat her wings fast enough to ease the rapture of her being. Sixteen thousand times a minute, the tiny silver pinions beat the air—but this was not enough. For she had never known, and would never know, the sadness of winter.

Even the primrose and the daffodil have memories of cold silences. The nightingale cannot sing until the glory of her voice is rounded by the wistful knowledge that summer dies.

But this bee had been born on a day when Persephone stole back from Hades, smiling so that black trees, gray grass and ruffled birds stirred like sleepers kissed. To begin on such a day is to enter life with warmth that never ebbs, but throws its own sunshine outwards from within.

Not merely would she never know of winter—she would never see a world beyond the summer solstice, sorrowfully declining into cold, darkness and decay. Life, to her, was a lovely procession of increasing summer days always growing more beautiful. Each one was longer than the last, warmer and bluer; each night shorter and more genial; more flowers and more crowded the meadows and the hedges; the air became more sweet, and felt warmer and still warmer—like a lover's caresses; the birds were more voluble and ever happier; day by day, the earth more dearly unfolded its loving to exhibit new beauties to excite and new experiences to content. Perhaps Heaven is like that, with new loveliness disclosing and increasing for ever, and never a midsummer day to mark the tragic point of no return.

As she ascended with delirious swiftness into the speedwell blue of the spring sky, unable in utmost effort to spend all the joy that thrilled her exquisite, featherweight body, she saw falling away beneath her an oakwood set on a hillside across which sheep drifted continually like little clouds over a changeless sky.

Immediately, the bee's happiness was increased by the exhalation of delight from all the things that she could see, whose joy sprang from the same boundless source as her own.

Each separate blade of young grass was reaching upwards towards the sun. Among the infinite shapes and colors of these grasses, millions of insects were astir with wildest eagerness. Along the hedges, innumerable tiny leaves were secretly uncurling, thrusting off the dull cloaks that had hidden each one like a fairy queen in beggar's raiment. The faintest green mist across the treetops of the wood, like a vapor hiding a transformation scene, was caused by breaking buds, the spearpoints of spring's legions, shining as they marched in to free their own princess from the passionless grip of winter. The world was drenched with warmth, and things were moving everywhere; even the air itself seemed renewed, sweetened, more buoyant.

The air! Man has visions of flight—not the roaring progress of heavy, stinking iron machines, but that silent loveliness of gliding on outstretched arms that comes to everyone in dreams. Even that is but half-flight—a wingless, semi-nightmare movement with fear haunting it. Man crawls earthbound on leaden feet.

But this bee, as she darted swiftly away from the wood and down towards the river that curled in the distance like the blade of a silver scythe, rested on air and was part of its living lightness. Though her speed was over twenty miles an hour, she could stop suddenly, hover, fly backwards, climb at a tremendous pace, or proceed seven miles in an unresting flight. Seldom did her flights exceed a mile, but that was because of her eagerness to carry back food to the city to which she belonged.

Two pairs of diaphanous wings gave her the key to Heaven. A large pair of wings in front, a smaller pair behind them, both so little and fragile that a careless breath would blow them away if they were detached from the body, yet these wings possessed powers that man, after millions of years of evolution, has not been able to equal. One large pair of wings would give more flying strength than two smaller pairs; but one large pair would not fold down sufficiently to allow the bee to enter certain flowers, or to creep inside a honey cell. So the bee has two pairs of wings, which fold primly over each other when not in use. Each lower wing is fitted with a row of twenty microscopic hooks. When in flight these hook the two wings on each side together, so that they give the powerful, pulsating beat of one large wing.

Air sacs in the bee's thorax fill, when in flight, and make her buoyant. After she has been at rest some little time, the sacs empty, and when that has happened she has to take a short run and vibrate her wings so as to fill the air sacs before taking off.

Thus, when in the air, this bee was as light as a feather, but possessed of a swift intelligence and quivering eagerness; having alighted, the weight of her body and the tremendous grip of her feet enable her to make her way safely about on a flower swinging through enormous arcs at the top of a slender tree.

Straight as a bullet she flew down across the hillside towards the stream, her joyous hum adding a rhyme to the unending poem of sound that pervades the spinning world always, by day and by night. Though she could fly no faster, she could not go fast enough to satisfy her own lust of motion and to give out the joy of a secret knowledge she alone possessed.

Not the green immensity of the landscape from horizon to horizon, not the whole unending depth of the blue sky, could hold all the happiness she had in the knowledge of the Golden Tree.

Yet the world through which she winged her pathless way was almost impossibly beautiful. It would have looked heavenly to man. But in comparison with the bee, man sees but a segment of the landscape, with only the dimmest conception of its shapes and colors.

The bee has five eyes to his two, and these are not coarse, peering globules like ours, but miracles of godlike power and complexity. Compared with our rough-edged, faded perception, they must give godlike vision. Three simple eyes that see as well as ours are arranged on the vertex of the bee's head. Below them, in the same relative position as our own, are two compound eyes. In the worker bee each of these eyes has six thousand lenses, where our eye has but one.

Each lens is hexagonal—perhaps explaining why bees build hexagonal cells. Each shining black hexagon is but a one-thousandth part of an inch in diameter. The drone has thirteen thousand lenses in each eye. Twenty-six thousand lenses against man's pitiful two; and the drone has three other eyes as well. No man can imagine the sumptuous splendor such eyes must see in the shapes and colors of a summer day; yet man, in his blindness, despises "the lazy drone."

The eyes of the flying bee took in every detail of the world around her, and of the sky in which she flew. The shapes and angles of individual specks of dust upon the ground were precisely appreciated in their beauty. The pores of the young leaves on the hedges, the play of the sun on the rough bark of elms making a myriad lights and shadows, the particular curves of grasses, their texture and arrangement, the colors of the distant view and every separate wimple in the flashing stream could be minutely examined. So could a thousand insects on the earth and innumerable others in the air at varying distances in the depths of the spring sky. While appraising the shape of each of them, the bee could simultaneously consider the buds on miles of hedgerows surrounding village fields; without prejudice to the intent watch she kept on the course of her flight, she could at the same time look, as it were, deeply into each tight bud and consider its color and shape and the day when it would open its sweet store to her ravishment. She could watch the birds on all sides, for birds are often bees' enemies. Each ray of sunlight that glowed in the golden radiance of the morning could be joyously accepted, and perhaps analyzed into its primal colors, by twelve thousand glittering facets.

Man dreams of fairyland, but every bee must see it and live in it.

The smell of the bee's fairyland must be as adorable as its appearance. In her antennae are five thousand tiny "nasal" smell hollows. Instead of our fumbling sense, which tells us coarsely whether something held beneath our nose is pleasant or the reverse, the bee can detect the fragrance of a single apple blossom half a mile away, or tell crocus from jasmine, or distinguish between a far-distant clover head and the tiny flower of the lime tree.

She can do more than that. By some strange instinct of smell about which we understand nothing, she can tell by an hereditary memory whether man or beast is friendly to her people, or their enemy. In summer, a worker bee lives only about six weeks. The queen, from whom they are all born, may live three years. Yet it is a fact that man or animal which has befriended a bee colony in its need may go to that colony ten years later, and will be civilly received even on a day when others dare not approach. Thus, through a great gap of what man, not understanding it, parcels out as Time, a period which to these bees must equal several of man's centuries, the community remembers its friend; though how this remembrance is preserved, and by what identity the friend is recognized in the communal mind of a succession of many generations of bees, who number several millions in all, we do not know.

Possessed by the glory of the world, knowing all the scents of springtime of which man realizes but one or two, seeing all the colors and living movements of Nature awakening to reincarnate life, the bee, rapturous with the ineffable wonder of her mission, shot down into the valley along the side of the stream and into the Golden Tree.

The tree was what country people call "palm"—a variety of willow, covered with large opening buds, each one heavy in golden pollen. As yet, only the first of them were open, but on these the yellow dust was so thick that vagrant airs scattered it like sifted flour.

This "palm" pollen has an ancient name. It has been called bee-bread for many centuries—certainly back to the time of Shakespeare's merry England. The bee-bread pervaded the tree with a wonderful, exceedingly faint perfume, exciting even to human beings, and to the bee the very breath of existence. To her, the flame of gold that set the little tree glittering was the fire of immortal life. The dust that floated lightly down with each passing breeze was fairy treasure, and the place where she had found it shone in all the magic colors of the rainbow's foot.

She hurled herself onto the biggest of the buds, scattering a thousand golden grains; miserly of each one, as her all-seeing eyes watched them daintily descending, yet the wild joy of uncountable others brushing against her, drenching her with their perfume and smothering her bodily as she plunged among them and tossed them hysterically over her back, was sufficient compensation. Frantically grabbing this treasure and loading herself with it, she could bear to squander the lost gold because what was left was illimitable and unending.

On her hind legs were little pollen baskets, cunningly contrived by the Architect who fashions each tiny thing perfectly for its own purpose. These baskets were protected by lids of hair, and were so placed that the maximum disposable load could be placed there without spoiling the bee's delicate flying trim. Thus, while carrying a burden equal to a fair proportion of her own weight, she could make headway against the gusty winds and sudden, blinding showers of springtime without being overset and hurled to the cold ground, from which, if overloaded, she might never have risen again.

Seizing the blazing grains of pollen, she stuffed them into the baskets so fast that her movements could hardly be followed by human eye. Greedily she leapt from bud to bud, not waiting to strip one, but plunging to and fro like a poor man might who found himself suddenly in Ali Baba's cave, surrounded by heaps of rubies and pearls, sapphires and emeralds, and mountains of gold coins. Yet she filled her baskets methodically enough, and at tremendous speed. The sheer delight of her movements was evidenced by the way she rubbed her shoulders and head in the pollen, bowed to it, pirouetted and capered among it, smothering herself on head and back and legs with it, while never for one moment pausing in her avid gathering of the grains.

She was alone in the tree, save for a hedge fly who prinked saucily up to her; she struck at him in an exasperated way, without malice, and he jinked away with every muscle in his shimmering body glancing and laughing, came back, then darted off to investigate and torment some other thing.

The bee, who had filled her baskets brimming over, and moved jerkily with huge knobs of pollen behind her legs, paused for one deliberate second and savored her triumph. She was the first bee in that tree—the very first to discover this incalculable bounty of new bee-bread. Pollen had been brought in, from aconites and crocuses and other flowers, but that was only the earnest of a harvest to come. Now it was here—enough pollen to renew completely the community assurance of life into the summer. She who had never known a winter was profoundly stirred by an instinctive sense of wondering achievement and reassurance. Her life had always been warm, well-fed and happy, but now in some mysterious manner she knew that life would be so for thousands of bees not yet born. This deep realization of continuity brought overwhelming content.

With a whir, she sped upwards again into the sky. Using that uncanny sense of direction that enables a bee to fly directly home though she may have zigzagged over fifty meadows, this little pioneer darted over the hillside towards the oakwood from which she had come. Exulting, she beat her way through the enormous hemisphere of sun-illuminated sky, passing scattered cottages, a sheepfold, a group of trees, hedges, and gray outcrops of rocks on the hill. At one point, she deviated from her arrow-like line to avoid a blackbird's nest that was, to her, as big as a cavern, and guarded by two black dragons not at all impartial, in the stresses of nestingtime, to a succulent bee or two. And so at last she rose over the brown woodland, and looked down on the exquisite patterning of gray and black and brown and silver twigs and grave branches and seamed trunks that were, for her, the environs of home.

It seemed to her that she must seek one of those twigs, and cling there in exhaustion. Pride had made her fill those pollen baskets far too full for such a fickle day of blue and cloud. The wind that was so warm grew suddenly cruel. The sun vanished; and with its passing, all the scurrying little life of the grasses and the trees and the multitude of flying insects—vanished. Only the bee was left, struggling wearily along with a load too heavy for her to bear.

Fear pervaded her, gray and cold and clinging as a fog. Not fear for herself, since the bee's thought is always for the community it serves; but fear lest the little furry babies in their waxen cradles should be denied that new pollen she was carrying; fear lest her thousand sisters should not, after all, be the first to rape the Golden Tree. Her eyes, watching for the familiar aerial road down between the branches to the city that was her home, became aware of tiny shrinking movements of the partly unfolded leafbuds, as the cold touched them.

The mating birds that on her outward journey were playing everywhere, have vanished, too. The pollen in the two baskets, that looked so gay and splendid, grows intolerably heavy. The bee knows that if she stops to rest, in this sudden chill, she may never be able to fly again. If she does not rest, the strain of overloaded flight in the cold will kill her.

Indomitable in her consciousness rises the pride that the first pollen brings. The first load—the divine renewal of the promise of unlimited bee-bread, so that the race may be renewed. At last, fierce flutter, a triumphant downward swoop into an oak tree long ago split by lightning, then a long pause with body rhythmically swinging to gain strength for the ceremony that is the reward not only of her own sacrifice of life but of the dogged struggle of her race to survive into the summer once more.

A sudden glorious leap into the hole which is the mouth of the bee colony's nest. Instantly two dark, fierce sentry bees dart from the hole and cross their antennae before the newcomer as sentries might cross swords. She stands quite still. The sentries quiver, waiting to pounce and tear off her head, wings, legs. There is no pity; the intruder dies.

But this is no intruder; she has the community smell. Each colony of bees has its own identifiable odor, and the sentries rarely or never make a mistake, even when hundreds of bees each minute race in and out. The pollen-bearer runs past swiftly into the heart of the tree. It would be dark to us, but the bee's splendid compound eyes can gather as much light there as we do in the sunshine. She goes along the rough way swiftly, and jumps suddenly up on to a hanging honeycomb, flanked by another and another, and shimmering and murmuring with thousands of the little winged people of this hidden city. Along the golden, waxy streets she goes, hurling bystanders right and left, and proudly claims her place at the very center of the nest, where hundreds of nurses are busy with furry baby bees.

The newcomer pays no attention whatever to the various urgent activities around her. She selects an empty cell, and convulsively starts to unload the pollen from the baskets on her legs into the golden storehouse of the comb. Only worker bees have these baskets; neither queens nor drones

collect pollen, so they have no need of them. This bee works
furiously fast. She stumbles like someone frantic to be first
in a race. And so, indeed, she is, for she is winning a race
whose prize is life for posterity. Death is by her side already,
dragging at her tired members; her triumph is that now it
comes to her alone. It is as if, in dying, one could save—or
condemn by failure—all humanity.

The young bees round her are being born in hundreds
every day. Their food is almost gone. Pollen from scattered
spring flowers is not enough. The golden surplus jealously
stored from the blossoms of yesteryear is spent. A mass sup-
ply of new pollen had to be found, or starvation and extinction would ensue.

Hardly waiting to rid herself of all her load, with the
fairy dust still clinging to her legs, she begins to caper in
a golden saraband.

Now she is the prima ballerina of the springtime, the
harbinger of life renewed. She spins up the combs in her
dance of death, but for those others, the little furry ones,
the pearly grubs, the eggs, the millions yet unborn, it is the
Dance of Life.

She waves to the right in a curving swing, then waltzes
swiftly back again to the newly loaded cell, where she
starts to pirouette, swinging her tail and abdomen as a jazz-
ing Negress swings her hips. The violent dancing and the
quivering beat of her wings wafts the exciting pollen
fragrance about the hive as an acolyte swings the incense
from his censer. Away goes the dancer on the wings of
delight, now to the left and back again, now repeating before
the new pollen cell another whirl of priestly worship.

Across and across the crowded combs, the message swiftly

runs. More and more workers look up from their jobs, entranced as if their lives depended upon what they saw—as,
indeed, they do. First some, then many, race towards the
new pollen cell. Many of them try to touch the dancer with
their quivering, eager antennae. In a minute the colony is
in commotion.

And then unfolds the strangest part of this hidden mystery.
Some of the forager bees detach themselves from the dance,
drop to the floor and race out of the entrance and away
across the sky, straight towards the "palm" tree in the distant valley. One after another they emerge and whirl upwards and vanish like small, singing bullets.

How do they know where she came from? Bees cannot
communicate by sound anything except emotions. A hum
of a certain pitch means danger, a low hum signals food,
and so on; but they cannot indicate detail in this way,
though many believe that they can "talk" by a sort of
semaphore with their antennae.

Did the pollen-bringer, who is still dancing exultantly
along the combs, explain where her pollen came from? Or
does a race memory record where the first trees bloom? We
do not know. Other pollen-gatherers return, fully loaded,
while their sister is still whirling up and down the golden
streets, stretching this final glory to its remorseless limit.

She grows tired and moves slowly. The others are streaming, now, towards the Golden Tree that she will never see
again. She drops to the floor eventually, exhausted, with her
last clear duty in her mind. Two hundred yards away, near
a dark pool of the river, is the bees' graveyard. Each bee
colony has its own graveyard, to which, when other work
permits, all dead bees found in the hive, and such brood as

must for some reasons be discarded, is carried; while those flying bees who can get so far go there at the last to die.

There the pollen-gatherer flies, unloaded but heavy, and glides down on to a grass stem. With slow and fateful steps, she climbs to the very top of it, and there clings, quivering slightly, and looking upwards into the depths of blue. The sky looks lovely to us. To those myriad-faceted eyes, with their passionate delight in color, it must seem Heaven indeed.

As the day grows colder, her grip on the grass stem will fail, and she will drop into forgetfulness. But because of her, a steady stream of bees is pouring through the sunshine to the "palm," which thrums like a thing alive with the noise of happy labor. As each bee returns loaded to the golden city, she darts with her head into a cell near that in which the first pollen was stored, and repeats faithfully the movements of the first joyous announcer. After an hour, the Grand Dance of the Bee-bread is in full career. Regiments of dancers swing and bow, turn and weave and pass, clapping their silver wings. The oak hums as if all the machinery in fairyland was at work within. The sound is eloquent of an intensity of happiness and fulfillment which anyone who has heard it can never forget.

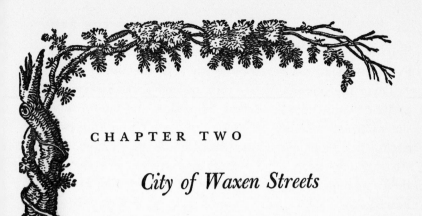

CHAPTER TWO

City of Waxen Streets

THE city inside the oak tree was peopled, at this time, by some sixty thousand winged inhabitants. This city was the size of a cushion. In daytime it was pervaded by a translucent, pale light, a kind of golden warmth, as if it were an enormous glowworm. The light filtered through the hole which was the city's main gate to the outer world, and also through some knife-width crevices in the side of the great trunk. The crevices had been filled by generation after generation of bees with a transparent propolis glue, which they gathered from pine and plum trees. This glue had set very hard, like dull glass. When the sun was setting, its rays struck horizontally through the propolis, and some trick of the angle divided the light rays into spectra, so that, at those times, the city was drenched with a silent radiance of divided red, orange, yellow, green, blue, indigo and violet, crossed by a number of fine black lines. This miracle happened especially after a rainstorm, and was one of many wonders of the place.

The streets of the city were bordered with hanging combs of lustrous yellow wax. These combs were spade-shaped, and hung at an exact distance from one another—just that distance required to enable bees to work on opposite faces of a comb without impeding each other; and the distance did not vary so much as one-eighth of an inch.

Very wonderful, they were, these intricate plates of masoned gold. On each side of them were thousands of hexagonal cells, whose walls were only one-thousandth part of an inch thick when they were newly built; yet in a single comb there hung more than ten pounds of shining honey, and over them crawled thousands and thousands of urgent bees.

Every cell was a perfect and regular hexagon. The hexagon shape, more than any other, gives the greatest capacity and resistance with the minimum expenditure of material and building labor. Man does not use the hexagonal shape for building, but the bee builds perfectly. This shape, too, freely admits the body of the tiny builder, leaving no space wasted, and because each cell supports the other, enables the masons to reduce the thickness of the walls to that of the thinnest paper, while conceding nothing in strength.

In the center of the nest some of the cells were almost imperceptibly larger than others. All the rest were half an inch deep and one-fifth of an inch wide, never varying even by a hair's breadth. But, here and there, patches of cells occurred which were one-quarter of an inch wide. In the first, when necessary, young worker bees could be cradled; in the larger cells, drone bees could be born. In the secret heart of this nation of perfect builders existed an intelligence which perfectly controlled the proportions of the population—so many workers and so many drones, according to the needs of the community. These needs were themselves conditioned by the state of the weather and the dates of opening of certain flowers. Yet the eggs from which the bees were born had to be laid, in the case of the workers five weeks, and with the drones almost six weeks, before the bees would fly freely from the tree. Who could guess the weather six weeks ahead? Who could foretell the opening of flowers, which vary their blossoming according to fickle sunshine, wind and rain? None knows. Yet on the answering of such questions, the life of the bee colony depends.

At this early Easter season there were no drone eggs and no baby drones in those waxen cradles that were ever so little bigger than the rest. Food rationing has become a part of man's existence, and he is angry; but with these little people it has always been so grave a matter that all whose usefulness is ended are thereupon put to death; nor are any born for whom the golden storehouses contain no food. Rationing? Birth-control? Here they are necessities for the race's survival. So, each autumn, when Nature's bounty of honey is withdrawn, all the males are destroyed; and until that bounty returns in full, no more of them are allowed to be born, though young workers are tenderly created.

So, on this day in springtime, baby bees were being born in the center of the city, and nurses fussed and crooned about them; but all were sterile females, dedicated to the task of carrying onward the cherished fire of life at which these impotent creatures might never fully warm themselves.

Perhaps they had their compensations. For the streets of gold were delicate and beautiful; those wondrous eyes could clearly see every one of the tens of thousands of exquisite cells. And, within them, the blue-white eggs lying row on row—the larvae, newly hatched, whose length is only one-fifth of the diameter of the cell (and that cell only one-fifth of an inch wide); the bigger larvae; the young brood sacredly sealed; the mysterious nymphs lying like Sleeping Beauties inside a half-transparent golden coffin that enclosed not death but budding life; and, here and there, the shining, entranced, eager faces of the newly born bees which, having bitten their way half out of the cells, were rapidly turning their heads from side to side, enthralled at this first sudden sight of teeming life.

Out upon the combs a thousand activities were in progress. Here, groups of young nurses swiftly attended to the needs of the grubs, feeding them with a special salivary liquid, guarding them with outthrust shoulder from accidental hurt from the thousands of hurrying citizens who passed endlessly up and down over the combs, and humming the steady cradlesong of the bees. There, a fierce, black-visaged old soldier bee, not a hair on its beetling and sturdy body, plunges its whiskers into a honey cell, after an arduous spell of sentry-go at the city gate; and if, as it raises its head from refreshment, the nurses glance its way, who can blame it if it cocks its whisker yet more fiercely, and rolls a languishing and magnificent black eye? Nursemaids and soldiers were ever thus.

Further out on the comb, the earnest masons work, repairing the ravages of winter, patiently cutting out mildewed walls and replacing them with bright, sound new ones, or tramping steadily inwards towards the brood, bearing the waxen coffin lids which seal the cells in which the larvae sleep, and sleeping, go so near to death as to shed their worn outer husks and emerge, not souls indeed, but perfect bees.

Here a bee stores pollen, there one gives up a load of precious honey; some are fanning, some cleaning house; here, one combs its wings, intent on beauty; there, a water-carrier hurries past; afar off, a circle of maids of honor surrounds the almost magic figure of the queen.

This is no common city. Man cannot air-condition his cities, but bees vary temperature, humidity, even the very breezes that ventilate the golden ways. Outside, the sun may smite the ground till the grass shrivels on the burned earth; or a flurry of pouring snow may turn the calendar topsy-turvy and bite the blackened leaves from the trees; but here within the city, the temperature is always that of a very hot summer day, and the air is always fresh and sweet with the honey scent of ten thousand flowers.

Nor can any dirt or refuse harbor here. In midsummer, more than two hundred thousand tiny, restless feet come and go unceasingly; labors are performed with an intensity and eagerness that no human project can equal; the little winged figures transport enormous loads, perform prodigious tasks; pollen is spilled, and honey, dust and propolis and water and fragments of wax; flies are killed, perhaps, or bloody combats fought with wasps, when wings, heads and legs fly this way and that; but never a speck is left to soil this perfect place.

Even while such a contest is being fought, the wings and limbs amputated and flung down are being collected and removed by cleaners almost fanatical in their zest. Day and night unceasingly, the whole of the city is swept and cleansed and polished—the waxy masonry is licked and shone with a thousand furry tongues. Nothing that can be moved, whether whole or after being torn to pieces, nothing that is not sweet and clean as the bees and the flower-honey on which they live, is permitted to rest in this city of golden streets.

And this task is often extended. When the flowers of the meadows are giving honey lavishly, or when the great lime trees in the churchyard are covered with amber bloom, fresh undertakings are begun. Dauntless teams of bees strike out a line for a new street of the city. Relentlessly, they advance into the rotting wood of the oak's middle, bite out fragments small as sawdust, and hurl all feverishly behind them. As the pigmy miners cut their way forward through the darkness, tireless gangs of others seize the dots of riven wood, that are, to them, great logs, and stagger down with them across the combs and over the backs of bees working at other tasks, and pass the dark sentries at the gates, and drag their burdens to the edge of the tree, and fling them down with joy to the ground below. A pile of oak-dust grows there steadily, and humps itself higher each year as the waxen streets drive further; and in the springtime, out of the pile of rotted wood, there grows a primrose that adds its drop of clear, translucent honey to the store within. Out of the strong once more comes forth sweetness, as it was so many centuries ago in a love-story that is half-forgotten.

The same mysterious wisdom that guides the colony in the forecasting of its children directs them, also, in the exact science of sculpturing the waxen ways. Tireless little workers direct their furious energies with the mathematical precision of skilled engineers. They cut tunnels and drive saps; much of the wood must be carried out grain by grain, but more of it is removed in large chips bigger than the bees themselves, each one scientifically cut away from the main mass, and then seized in the claws of two or three or more bees, and dragged down to the runway leading to the city gates. And there, two of them seize the big piece of rough wood, and suddenly mount the air with it, flying perfectly together and gripping it between them as they fly. They pass out through the gates, where the sentries savagely sweep all other traffic into the corners or aside; they carry the wood sturdily five or ten yards from the tree, their wings beating frantically, though their pace is almost that of the snail; and there they release the load, spin round vaingloriously, and return for more.

Cunningly planned, the combs in the new streets, as in the old, hang from above, and never reach the floor of the orifice. They are perfectly rigid, despite the softening heat and the passing of the masses of little winged folk to and fro across them. Under them is a clear space, required to facilitate cleansing operations about the city; at each end of the combs is a corridor so that the workers can pass round from comb to comb without having to descend to the passageway beneath. For the most part, the combs hang perfectly regular and unbroken. But here and there has been left a passage hole through which nurses and honey-gatherers and pollen-bringers and water-carriers and soldiers and newborn babes and ragged crones, and perhaps even the queen and her retinue, pass and repass about their various activities.

This, then, was the City of the Bees. Up and down the fair land in which it belonged were hundreds of thousands of other waxen cities, each one as exquisite. In the fields and woods and gardens of the round world, in roofs, in trees, in hives and skeps and boxes, in discarded kettles and hedges and caverns and hung from the branches of trees were

millions more of them, such myriad millions as cannot be
counted. Each of them was a world in itself, fiercely, mercilessly intent on the continuance of its own race, though
hedged about with destructive giants and overwhelming
natural catastrophes and teeming tiny enemies, and the wafts
of invisible dread diseases. In each city there was the same
law; death to all who threaten the race; instant, selfless im-
molation if that will serve the race; work, such work as kills
within five or six weeks, if that will feed the race; the chill
touch of extinction at the very moment of sexual consummation so that will breed the race; a life, unnaturally long,
never warmed with sunshine or comforted with color or
companionship since that shall mother the race; a living
death through winter's cramping cold since only so the race
may see another summer break in cream and crimson along
the hedges and the fields.

So it is today. So it was when Jesus Christ was teaching
on the dusty Syrian hills. The Romans plowed the ruins
of Carthage with salt, but the bees, fierce, persistent, evasive,
preserved their golden cities safe. When Ptolemy was found-
ing his wonderful lost library at Alexandria, the bees were
building streets of just the same hexagon-walled, even-spaced
combs as they use now. Israelitish spies escaping flushed
from whore-bed reported a land flowing with milk and
honey. Perhaps the splendid complex eyes of the bee observed the first man lift his hairy hands from the slime and
painfully turn his troubled face to an unanswering sky.

Then, and before then, just as today in the oak tree in
the wood below the sheep-cropped hillside, dramas as vivid
and poignant as man's were being played out in these tiny
cities to which man never gave a thought. Passion, pathos

and the mystery of beauty do not belong to man alone. Amid the green and gold of Nature, these tiny creatures, too, are the sport of Love and Death, know hunger and desire and fear, and lay down their lives for their friends.

As their race had done from time before man and beyond man's comprehension, so the little winged people in the oak did today. Their queen walked stately through the masoned ways, attended by adoring maids, and guarded by troops faithful unto death. Her people gathered the sweetness of summer from the hearts of a million flowers. They plunged into bloody war. They watched each princess's love story, set in the bluest heights of Heaven, with Pan-pipes playing the wedding march. They knew the pain of hibernation, and passed from that dim, remembering dream into the sunlit halls of life once more.

And so the children of their race will do when the oak and the wood and the village are gone, in some age hidden yet in the blue distance of Time, when perhaps man's last footprint shall have faded from the dust.

CHAPTER THREE

The Little People

To watch a community of the little winged people is like looking at a human city through the wrong end of a telescope that has been endowed with magical clearness, so that every activity, and even every gesture, becomes vivid and meaningful. Yet there are such vital differences from any human race that ever existed, that the golden town weaves a magic of its own.

In the springtime, when the Dance of the Bee-bread took place, the society was composed entirely of females. There was the queen, as strictly constitutional as any progressive human royalty; and all the rest were her daughters. This is motherhood beyond compare. Yet the innumerable offspring will commit matricide—and regicide—if they are alarmed, using a method so tender and so careful that no philosopher can decide whether it is deliberate, or takes place in a wild surge to protect the being from whom all sprang, and who should outlive them all, and many a generation after them. If this thing must be, then tens of thousands of her daughters enclose their queen and mother in a suffocating embrace. They do not bite, they dare not sting; but, each clinging tightly to the other in a velvety-black tossy-ball, they stop her breathing, nor will they release her till her slender body shall fall, useless and vacant, and thence be swung away through the air on its last journey to the colony's graveyard.

And there is something strange in this; for, when the queen leads a swarm from the traditional home out into the hottest sunshine of midsummer, and that swarm settles on a bough or against a wall, once more the queen is placed in the center of the mass of moving bees, and tightly packed there; but then she is safe, can breathe and have her being, and will emerge presently, capable of accompanying her children two or three miles to a new dwelling, passing as swiftly through the air as if she had just taken wing after a honeyed feast.

This is a queen in the ancient tradition. Mated with her own brother, she sees around her in all her long lifetime, exceeding by perhaps six or eight times that of even the longest-lived of her children, no other people except her sons and daughters. In her solitary person, she carries the destiny of all. Yet, at the whim of her children, she can be deposed and may be slain, perhaps with no provision for a successor, so that all, then, must perish. At the very height of summer, and of her peerless dominion, there may be about her more than a hundred thousand of her daughters, and perhaps two or three hundred sons; and these are but a handful of the progeny that in her lifetime she sees born, at work, and then dying. What a universe of sorrows would be here, if indeed she can sorrow; for her destiny is not only to rejoice at several million births from her own fair body, but to see millions of her children die while she, godlike, must go on from generation to generation. In the autumn, she must watch her sons slain by their sisters; in the winter, if food is failing, she must eat while her children, score by score and hundred by hundred, plunge their heads in agony into empty honey cells and starve to death; in the spring-time, when the air is full of the throbbing song of mating birds, this queen must send out her little ones amidst the snow winds to seek for sustenance, knowing that most of them will never return; and in the height of summer, if bee war comes, it is her fate to watch all die before she herself may accept the fatal stroke.

For the others there is the sunlight, the glory of a thou-sand flooding colors, the wonder of a million scents, the caress of the summer air, the sight of orchards in fullest blow, the taste of water on warmed stone, the infinite of the blue Heaven in which to play. For her, none of these things. Of her own will, she must remain forever captive in the dimness of the golden city!—not even the silver mirror of the Lady of Shalott is permitted her; she may not look out-side upon the changing world, nor so much as walk to the city gates to taste unlicensed air.

She and her children—what sort of creatures are they? Man believes himself fearfully and wonderfully made; but he is clumsy compared with these little things, whose in-dividual weight is no more than that of a petal of apple blossom, and of whom it takes five thousand to weigh a single pound.

Look at the crowding citizens of the waxen streets, and you see tiny dark bodies covered with hairs. Some of these hairs are the most sensitive imaginable organs of touch. Others are brushes. Some are clothing. Many serve the purpose of protection. Some are gatherers of pollen. Some are ornaments.

Look at this head, not much bigger than a grain of dust. Its five eyes are only the first of its wonders. Do you see the two antennae? By these, the bee conveys emotions, needs, desires, threats. In a worker bee, each antenna has twelve supple joints; a man's arm seems clumsy by comparison. This tiny head has three pairs of jaws, and a tongue which is a miracle of perfection, and carries out tasks of infinite complexity.

The three pairs of legs which support the glimmering body are also equipped for special tasks. Here is a curry-comb of stiff hairs, there a spur with which to remove pollen balls; this nine-jointed leg is made to collect pollen or propolis; it forms jaws that help to load the pollen baskets, and has hairs essential in the architecture of wax. This tiny foot, so small that it can hardly be seen by man's coarse eye, is five-jointed, and carries formidable claws. Between the claws is a cushion, which secretes a gum so that the bee can walk on any smooth surface, even upside down.

Breathing takes place through gills in the sides of the body, which may be said, almost, to be one single lung; through these orifices, air sacs can be filled to assist flight. The fairy body is clad in a sort of scale armor. It is tough armor, and it has another purpose as well; in the ventral plates, the wax that is essential for bee community life is secreted.

The bee is just as wonderful inside its minute body. It is intricate almost beyond belief. The sting alone, which looks so insignificant, seems more like a weird and beautiful flower, when man's clumsy eye, examining it, is, by the aid of a microscope, brought to something like the analytical perfection of the bee's eye. When the sting is used in anger, it comes quick as a lightning flash; yet it is never used until the surface to be penetrated has been tested with sensitive feelers, ending in nerve points that tell the attacker just how deep the barb can be plunged into the victim. In such processes as this, man's conception of time is elephantine; what seems to him but a split second gives the bee time enough carefully to feel the surface, and then to select any thinner part of it, and so to plunge in the sting.

Bees, it seems, know quite well that to sting is to court death. Rarely, indeed, can the sting be withdrawn. Its barbs grip the pierced surface, and through a blow, or often because of the bee's own agonized or furious motion, sting and entrails are torn out, and the attacker crawls away to die. In combating any creature of its own size, or a little bigger, the bee dreads to sting; it fights ferociously, instead, with claws and jaws. But when mouse or badger, man or ox or even elephant, threatens the colony, ten thousand stings are tensed for the assault, and, if need be, ten thousand lives flung away with no more care than one. A fine needle, by comparison with this sting, is as thick as a crowbar would seem beside the needle. Nor is the sting a simple thing; a sheath makes the first penetration; then darts drill in and out faster than the human mind can conceive; then poison pours down the darts, as they deepen the hole that has been made.

At the city gates, as one enters this golden place, stand the sentries. These are old bees worn in the wars. They are selected specially for their abnormal quickness and strength. Their task is to examine everything that enters, and to kill all strangers. Each colony has its own distinctive smell; no matter how many flowers may have been visited, no matter if the bee has rolled in pollen till its back is mantled with glowing dust; yet the sentries cannot be deceived. In and out of these gates, at the heart of a summer day, fly tens of thousands of bees. Many hundreds may come and go in one minute; but never a stranger can pass, never a bee may enter without being examined by the half-dozen quivering sentries, each one ready to launch, like a thunderbolt, a fatal blow.

Just inside stand the fanners, whose task is to ventilate the city. They are poised with claws gripping the ground firmly, and wings vibrating so fast as to be invisible. There is no random labor in this; everything is planned; line upon line, the fanners stand, to keep the air currents moving exactly at the velocity and in the directions which the city needs. When honey is put in the cells, it contains more water than may safely be allowed to remain in it; the bees raise the temperature and drive off the moisture, and the damp air is continually driven out by the fanners while a current of fresh, dry air is drawn in and circulated round the combs. To complete a pound of sealed honey, the bees must evaporate between half a pint and one pint of water from the cells and send it out of the hive. A fatiguing task this fanning must be; but it achieves, by labor, just as much as man can do with machinery, and it is infinitely adjustable to weather conditions and to the city's requirements.

In the golden streets are the nurses, young bees not yet permitted to make honey flights, but none the less busy with work just as important as that of the food-gatherers themselves. This is the task of giving the warmth of their bodies to hatch the eggs and lavishing care on the baby bees.

For three days the egg must be tended; then an infinitely tiny grub appears. So far, it has fed upon the substance of the egg. Now, it is tenderly cared for by the nurses, who rear it on a substance perfected in their own salivary glands. After about three or four days more, a tiny amount of semi-digested honey and pollen is added to the food in the golden cradle. On the ninth day from the laying of the egg, if it is in a worker cell, the cradle is well stored with food, and sealed with a porous capping of wax and pollen, through which the little living thing inside can breathe. For thirteen days more, the nurse bees guard the cell and keep it precisely at the correct warmth—too much would scald the inmate to death, too little would make it die of cold, and the variation is but a few degrees either way. For thirteen days, in its mysterious solitude, the little creature is working its willful way towards life, towards the sunshine and the flowers—and towards eventual death.

With what pains, perhaps, does it cast off one skin, and then another and another? Who can say that each of these changes is not itself a death, and a rebirth? With each change, like some soul growing nearer and nearer to Heaven's perfection, it discards a fleshly tabernacle, and emerges more and yet more beautiful. From a blunt larva it becomes a strange, crude-shaped insect, only half alive. From that, it changes to a nymph. And so, change after change ensuing, and this, perhaps, in the mind that is so painfully evolving, taking aeons of unknown time, at last a bee is born.

It stirs. With folded wings and close-clasped feet, it is a perfect thing; God has produced another little life. The nurses hurrying about the combs rejoice; perhaps they reach

out eagerly towards it as the newborn bee, impatient for all
the joys and agonies of life, bites its way suddenly through
the paper-thin golden barrier that stands between it and
every adventure of existence. As the little creature crawls
out, looking about upon the world and preening its wings,
the nurses dart into the cell and clean it, and prepare it
for the immediate reception of another egg—one more step
in the unending cycle of generation.

The furry baby needs little other growth; it is practically
as big as the veteran bees who are loading honey into cells
nearby with an urgency that is the sharper because they
know their race is almost run. It springs into life full-fledged.

It plunges its head into a honey cell and drinks the nectar
of the summer blooms. It walks the combs, examining, marveling, learning. After a while it goes out, blindly attracted
to the wonder of the sunshine. Its wings unfold; and with
a humming song of triumph and delight, it climbs the air
and looks down upon a lovely earth. Up and down before
its dwelling, in and out among the trees and grasses and
flowers it goes, remembering once and for all every land-
mark, charging that strange sense which humans have got
only so dimly, which will forever afterwards say which way
lies home.

A few hours of play; then, in its turn it becomes a nurse.
And, after nursemaiding, the cycle moves relentlessly on;
the next stage of life is that of architect of the city streets;
at about fourteen days old, unless chosen for sentry work,
another stage is reached when honey gathering is begun. A
few weeks, only, maybe, to taste the glories of the world, to
see the sun climb and sink, and help the flowers unfold; and
then comes the end foretold when first life stirred within

the egg that was itself scarce bigger than a grain of that dust
to which we must all return.

In this insect life, passions surge as in our own. There is
no mating love, no jealousy or greed, no comradeship of
the sort we know; but there is hunger, fear, anger, pain,
and certainly delight more keen than ever humans know.
And, as likely as not, vice and sin as well. This creature,
bred of the sweetness and innocence of flowers, may become
a robber and a murderer, or may suffer the cruelties of
such; the gamut of the emotions can be run by bee as well
as man, and temptations shake them both as mercilessly hard.

CHAPTER FOUR

The Orchard

ENTRANCED, the oakwood waited for the dawn. All through the night, it had been populous with tiny stirrings and scufflings on the ground, in the trees, through the cold, clear air. Moths had worshiped in the moonlight, infinitely soft and gentle. Rabbits had scuttered among the weeds, and vanished; and then, afterwards, the fox had stolen by like a sliding shadow. Owls had passed and repassed silently as ghosts. A badger, idly rooting round the trees, stood transfixed for a moment, so barred in black and silver that a sleepy pheasant, roosting in the green blackness of a fir, stared straight at him with a shining, golden eye that suddenly caught the light, but saw nothing.

Then, as at a signal, all sounds ceased.

Where, a moment earlier, there had been busy life, nothing was visible now except crowding trees standing bewitched in slender, dark enchantment. Animals, birds, insects had vanished, as though some Presence too holy to be looked upon could be heard advancing gently through the wood. Invisibly, but none the less certainly, it came, enshrined in a gentle movement of the night air; and passed on over the horizon and so across the world.

Where it had passed, a change came. The horizon there grew clearer. Indigo tree and hedge took on, at their edges, the faintest pale radiance. The fields had been a black sea, but now slowly began to shimmer in rebirth, as though the spirit was returning to them. A linnet uttered a single note, which, like the rap of a conductor's baton, charged the air with intolerable suspense. The air itself, which had been sleeping, moved delicately to life, and a million young leaves stirred.

The sky took on an evasive radiance, first of clouded silver, then here and there of palest rose. The linnet chirped wildly, a blackbird piped and was still; and then, all at once, the bird-haunted hedges were alive with song. As though it had been waiting for this, the sun glowed in majestic silence across the shoulder of the hill, and its level rays touched tree-tops and grasses with radiance that picked out each leaf and blade, and threw pools of blackest shadow behind trunks and molehills.

The world awoke. The creatures of the night, that had so suddenly hidden themselves, hurried clumsily home. Innumerable living things stirred; birds moved briskly about the hedge-tangles, seeking commanding eminences from which to sing still louder; insects and animals among the grasses and in and out of the leafmold of the wood went anxiously about the task of hunting breakfast.

The steady beam of the rising sun reached the oak, in which the golden city was already astir. For the night, the little winged people had clustered together in a tight mass, like a ball of shimmering treacle, so as to lend each other an embrace that should defy the night's chill. As the golden finger of light crept further through the city gates, and the smell of morning air rose among the combs, a bee detached herself from the cluster and dropped lightly to the trodden way which led out into the world.

She stood there, with wings quivering, as if in prayer; then darted joyously out and paused in the warmth on the edge of the cleft tree. Her body moved rhythmically as she observed the splendor of the growing day. Then, as suddenly as if propelled by an explosive charge, she was bounding through the air, and away towards the river's edge.

This river, hardly wide enough yet to deserve a name, chuckled and rippled through the wood, flashing a silver shoulder over a tiny fall, spreading sinuously into a smooth pool here and there, glinting and gobbling and shivering and boasting, gliding silently through a thicket, and so aslant across the lower slope of the hill, between rows of willows into the village and thence, past lichened towns and roaring cities, to the sea.

Over the river, the bee hovered, then darted down and settled in a place where broken sunlight showed like a handful of gold coins flung on to the leaves. A minute later she was soaring up again, violent with eagerness, heading back for the oak.

This was the first of the water-carriers, beginning the most urgent outdoor task of the day. Life was stirring in the golden city; and life, especially baby life, needed sun-warmed water. On her flight back she was passed by other foragers speeding on the same task. One by one they dropped from the warmth and comfort of the cluster and adventured into the mild blue of the spring morning. As the sun climbed, the water-carriers grew more numerous.

Presently, an old bee, the diaphanous perfection of her wings a little shaded and ragged, and much of the glossy fur worn from her body, emerged past the sentries and paused on the brink beyond. She lifted her antennae this way and that, turned herself swiftly, darted a few steps, and tested the air again with those wonderful feelers that will pick out from ten thousand odors the waft of honey almost a mile away. A sentry, excited by this procedure, hurried crossly out, rudely butting the newcomer with his shoulder, and swung his own antennae to the breeze. They stood there together, moving their bodies gently; then the sentry sped back to halt and examine a returning water-carrier, and as he did so, the bee who had been so carefully prospecting the air suddenly took off.

Her direction was not to the stream. She sped along, straight as a bullet, high over the scattered buildings of a farmstead which occupied that part of the valley. It was almost surrounded by cattle sheds; at this time in the morning the yards were busy with the blunt and foreshortened forms of laboring men, the steaming shapes of horses, and a flurry of puppies observantly watched by a contented yellow dog. There were pigeons feeding there, too, hopping up irritatedly from beneath agricultural boots; chickens contested with them a losing scramble for grains of corn scattered in the mud; beneath an unattended cart a cat lurked with prim solicitude, unblinkingly watching the nearer doves, who, without seeming to take notice, watched her, too.

The bee saw all these things and many more. There was an insect painfully climbing a half-inch of straw, a mouse's bead-eyed head peeping from beneath the tiles of the farm roof, and a sparrow hawk hovering so high as to be only a dot overhead and avidly watching, too. The bee never varied her speed or line, but passed on. A few hundred yards on the other side of the house, she suddenly turned downward, and plunged into a billowing, wavering sea of purest pink, the apple blow of an old cider tree, in the midst of a considerable orchard.

Dropping among the blossoms that were each as big to her as a room might be to us, she came lightly to rest on a swinging, scented petal; and instantly was still.

Think of being so small that a single apple blossom seems like a cloud; think of swinging there in unshadowed sunshine, surrounded by a sea of dancing blooms that ripples away to every horizon. Think of seeing all this with eyes that would analyze every delicate vein in each curved silken petal, and of possessing the bee's profound and burning sense of the intensities and variations of colors, beside which our vision of even the wildest sunset is only a half-blind blur.

Think of the immensity of an apple orchard as it must seem to a bee, when the scent of all the blossoms, which is one scent to us, divides into innumerable perfumes, each different and each perfect, this from a Blenheim, that from a russet, another from a tall, slender pear tree; and when these scents are tasted, not through two nostrils, as in man, but through the five thousand nostrils of the bee.

Think of looking down from that airy couch of flushing silk, swaying as if the tree's vibrations in the wind were the movements of life, and seeing each rough trunk, silver and gray and brown in infinite variety, with hundreds of insects busy on each one, and then of analyzing, with the bee's wonderful sight, the perfect shapes and colors and fine activities of them all. And of the colors and shapes of all the grasses, like an army on the march.

Think of watching the sun through the bee's unshaded eyes, with the fantasies and glories of the solar flames visible in their changing shapes and colors, and royally promising all the summer days that are still to come.

For a moment the bee clung to the soft petal and looked round on the loveliness that hemmed her in, the dancing florets, the clasped buds, the blown flowers squandering their dainty petals lightly to the wind. Up and down, above, about, below, rising and falling, turning and bowing and delicately floating, the apple blossoms filled the air like a pink snowstorm tranced with its own beauty. From near and far, now, came a murmurous humming music, as hundred after hundred of the little winged people from the golden city floated down and swung themselves in the hearts of the rejoicing flowers, that seemed to close their warm, light petals in and welcome all who came.

The bee moved, turned her head towards the flower's heart, and crept within as happily as Love itself. Gently moving aside the swinging stamens, she opened the dainty bloom and began to taste the apple-blossom nectar.

If happiness can achieve the ultimate, this was perfection. There was no selfishness in it; the golden food that the gods drank on Olympus was being gathered, not for herself but for the children of the city. There was no greed or struggle, for in this single orchard was ten thousand times enough for all. An unclouded sun poured warmth among the trees, so that each blossom, secretly uncurling, offered itself ready for seduction.

For a few moments, basking in warmth, color and perfume and richly experiencing the climax of delight, the bee kept her place within the floret's heart. Then, backing swiftly out, she swung lightly into another perfect bloom.

This time she came not as guest but lover.

Daintily around her body she bore the golden pollen dust from the generous stamens of the cider tree. As she stooped, the flushed face of a young pippin blossom lifted itself towards her like a kiss. As she touched its loveliness, a breath of summer air sent it dancing upward in glee, and the silken petals closed about her in a swift embrace. She thrust gently inward, fascinated by the new perfume that the floret lavished spendthrift on its favorite. The bee's tongue shot out, sweeping backwards and forwards in delicate rhythm, the hairs of the tiny spoon at its extremity gathering nectar from the floret's very heart, and leaving there instead the gold-dust seed which, in that warm and secret citadel, would quicken and grow and give the orchard life and immortality.

At last, the bee's delicious task was done, and she crept from the sated flower, and passed on to another and another and another, bringing to each one the ecstasy of love's fulfillment, and taking from each a ransom of golden nectar.

More than one hundred of the apple florets were thus dearly ravished before her load of nectar was complete; and then, though it was as much as she could carry, it was in all only one-third of a drop. To gather a pound of honey, bees must make a combined flight that totals over fifty thousand miles, a distance that would girdle the earth twice. Forty thousand individual loads of nectar are required to

46672

gather a pound of honey; but a community such as that which occupied the golden city in the oak tree counts five hundred pounds of honey only a moderate summer's harvest.

On the sunny days from April to September, perhaps two thousand million flowers surrender their virgin hearts so that one colony of bees may live. To each flower the bee brings the sweet fulfillment of love, and the promise of its fruition. Without the little winged almsmen, a hundred thousand species of flowers would die away from the earth and be seen no more.

As the day grew hotter, the slumberous sound of the multitude of the bees in the orchard blossoms rose and increased till the air throbbed. The warmth drew the perfume from the florets, and opened branched treasure-houses of new ones. But the bees could not restrain their ardor, and clasped the buds, caressing them like lovers whose seductive touches might open the way to their desires. More and more bees came and went, not only all those who could be spared from the oak, but thousands from the farmstead's skeps and from distant hives, and from further afield still. The air above the sea of pink was thronged and tumultuous with glittering cohorts of argent-winged bees, and the perfume of new honey mingled intoxicatingly with the varied apple-blossom scents. Below, the blossoms became a blushing, silken bed of universal love, moving and murmuring as thousands of opening buds shyly surrendered their treasures to the caresses of the insatiable bees.

Midday passed, and as the bees grew tired, their humming lost its first avidity and took a more contented note like the lulling of a summer sea. Each bee kept flawlessly to the task of collecting honey of similar flavor, color and consistency.

It would have been unforgivable to mix the translucent, pale honey of the pear with the darker amber of the old russets. The same artistry caused the bees to keep the various kinds of honey in separate cells in the hive, no more mixing them than a vintner would mix Burgundy and claret.

Other creatures passed through the orchard. A rat wormed swiftly along a run in the tall grass. A pair of nesting chaffinches sported up and down a trunk, the cockbird shouting —"Twink, Twink!"—at the top of his voice. His nest, clad in silver lichen, was in a pear tree, but he never uttered his valiant call in that place, believing himself extraordinarily subtle because he made a great noise elsewhere; and his wife plainly thought him wonderful.

An early butterfly, splendid in black and scarlet, fluttered among the pink-laden branches like the herald of the Fairy Queen. Here and there, he clung to the rough bark of a tree, opening and shutting his wings as though to mark the periods of a proclamation.

Among the blossoms, the bees paid no attention to anything but their lovely task. No bee ever entered a flower while another suitor rested there, nor did one ever go where the sweet virginity was already rifled. A glance, a swift turn of the head, and another floret was selected. Round the orchard they thronged the air, mingling their two-way traffic as though thousands upon thousands of shuttles patterned an intricate silver web to make a gossamer mantle of invisibility.

In the city in the tree another ceremonial dance was in its wildest bacchanal fling. The honey-bearers were hastily placing their loads into cells, bowing before them, whirring their wings, folding them, turning their heads in mysterious

measure, swinging away together right and left, passing each
before her loaded cell, bowing, then pirouetting in magic
rapture like pagan priestesses before some garlanded altar
whose incense rose intolerably sweet and thrilling. Other
bees from all about lifted their heads and ran at the dancers,
striving to touch them as they went whirling past. While
some wove their course in the pale golden light, others
dropped, plummet-like, to the floor, and darted from the
entrance up the sky towards the orchard that was flushed
and shimmering as a sunset sea.

With godlike vision and godlike unconcern for the other
tiny actors on that crowded stage, the bees, as they swung
in the dainty florets, saw birds glancing through the
branches, dormice pattering between the grasses, enameled
scarabs killing one another, grasshoppers poised and vibrant,
spiders surfeited, and new-hatched flies shivering with desire
to taste the whole of life. The bees saw all these things, and
knew no emotion but longing for more and more and yet
more flushing stars of apple blossom going on for ever giving
out the fragrance of new honey that meant a renewal of the
race promise of eternal life.

CHAPTER FIVE

Oh, Queen! Live for Ever!

ON ancient hills, in fields of asphodel, the gods
walked among men; but in the bees' city of golden
streets a goddess was present always to comfort her
children, and in her wisdom to guide them in the ordering
of their lives.

Some of the bees, who had been born in the autumn and
watched the heather above the hillside flame like the table-
cloth of God, might, at the longest, live seven months. Those
born in the spring or summer would rarely know more than
seven or eight weeks of sunny life.

Far, far back in the dim mists of communal memory, beyond the life of the oldest bee, and for unnumbered generations away into the history of the past, the queen had always
been there. In what man calls time, she was nearly three
years old; but three years, to one who lives eight weeks, is
the span of eighteen lifetimes. To the bees it was as it would
be to us if we were ruled by a being who had known the
Vikings, and who would still be here centuries after we were
dust.

Truly, this queen belonged to the immortal gods.

More than this. To the little people of the city this gentle
goddess was the mother of all living, the creator of all those
of whom memory or even tradition told the story, the
matriarch of all, not merely of those who would be born
in foreseeable time, but of all who would ever be born.

None other among those tens of thousands of busy citizens carried within her body the mystery of perpetuated life.
While their queen lived, their future lived. If she died, without succession, they were but walking shadows waiting for
a silence that nothing should ever break until the furthest
edge of illimitable time. Though they had begun when
God first breathed life into the dust and slime of the empty
planets, though they had survived in slowly changing form
from trilobitic ancestors, escaped the sea scorpions and the
great fishes of the Azoic Seas, the reptiles of the coal swamps,
the cold that killed the dinosaurs, and the successive scarring
winters of the Glacial Ages, the claws of the bears and the
prehensile, hairy hands of primitive man, though they had
adapted and fought victoriously for existence for eight hundred million years . . . yet their story would end abruptly
and for ever if this immortal died and none succeeded her.

Such things happened—dread beyond all human comprehension. If a million men die, what of that? If, through
man's folly and wickedness in using for destruction forces
he does not understand, a hundred millions perish in a
moment, it is by comparison a little thing. So long as man
and maid survive, crouching in the crevice of a mountain
and holding to each other with trembling arms, human life
will go on. But in this little city, disease, accident or old
age may stiffen the dainty body of their goddess in death—
she who has been immortal for countless ages—and unless

the loss is repaired within six days the colony which has existed with an unbroken history longer than that of mankind, must perish utterly and never see another summer flush the earth with color.

Every year bee colonies die like this. Their pedigree is longer than that of men and apes, but it ends suddenly with no future for evermore. The queen perishes; perhaps she is snapped up on her wedding flight by a casual bird; maybe she is injured in her own guarded city by the fall of a pebble or a chip of wood whose destiny was written millions of years ago when the pebble was formed or the first oak sprang from the swamps. But if she dies, or if her fertility is damaged or naturally ceases, and no provision is made for her successor, within one week a blackness descends on that bee city, and from that day its people know that they will be expunged from the world without leaving any trace.

Most poignant of all, these little people may destroy their own queen in a panic struggle to shield her from harm.

The dreadful knowledge of their dependence on their goddess is apparent in their every movement as they surround her within the golden city in the oak. Where she passes, workers, no matter how busy or how raging, turn aside to open the way. In emergency she may walk over their bodies, and they take immense precautions not to cause her injury. She may walk beneath a living arch of them, and there they will stay, not merely protecting her with their bodies, but so doing it that the hurts which kill them do not even disorder her progress under them.

If she leaves the city they go with her, most of them, abandoning food, children, protection; where she goes they go, and where she stays, though it be in the heart of a furnace, there they cast themselves. Injury may send her reeling to the ground; then they form a protective mass above her to keep her warm and safe from the rain which they dread and which will kill them. If she is removed from them they run in terror to and fro and search minutely everything for yards around, pathetically moving great leaves to look beneath them, tearing with their jaws at pitiless wood or iron lest she be there. If they cannot find her they abandon the gathering of food, allow the baby bees to die of chill, refuse to eat, and pine to death.

As she goes about their city she is attended by adoring maids. These young bees, gentle and furry, chosen perhaps for their beauty and docility, try always to keep their heads pointed towards their goddess; they may be seen dearly encircling her, offering her the very choicest honey from their outstretched tongues, lovingly cleaning and caressing her shapely body, smoothing her exquisitely folded wings, but most of all standing round with worshiping eyes, returning thanks and giving praise for the immemorial wisdom with which she guides her people, and the immortal and ineffable love by which she creates them, serves them and carries for them the deathless flame which alone illumines their future.

What is she like, this golden queen? She is longer than her daughters, more slender than her sturdy sons: her wings are crossed on her back like the demure hands of a dreaming girl, instead of being vigorously outthrust like those of all her children. She has fewer of those glittering hexagonal facets to her eyes, for she is a goddess whose whole life is devoted to selfless service within the dim and dainty light of the golden city; once, perhaps twice in her lifetime, she may go out and see the flowers and feel the sunshine; but though she live thirty times as long as one of her daughters, those little golden interludes of perhaps five minutes each are all she may ever see of that lovely world to which she sends the others, all she may ever know in her own person of color and scent and form and the swaying rapture of flight.

Perhaps her little maids, yearning for their beloved goddess, spend their time telling her of everything they have seen—the colors of the sky, the perfect prettiness of flowers, the movements of leaves and of birds' heads, the minuet of pines in the evening air, the petting of the flower as its honey is taken, the depth and richness of a million heather bells, the taste of dew, the noonday radiance of the sea. They could tell her of the stealthy burgeoning of the world in springtime, the budding and shooting and sprouting, the dilation and sudden coloring, the glowing and flushing and scintillation, the tingling and thrilling; and the strength and depth and warmth of coming summer. They could describe to her who had never seen them the honeysuckle and the creamy dog rose, bluebells like fallen sky, the shapes of primroses, the translucent light and shade of a lime tree or the scent from the rose's heart. They could tell how the sun climbed from the dawn and sank to drowsy dusk.

While they told their magic tales of a world as remote from her as Heaven is from us, their slender goddess must never pause in her duty. At this time in the heyday of spring she would be creating perhaps three thousand children in a single day.

Moving from cell to cell with movements gentle and sweetly dignified, which mark her out from all her bustling family, she must examine each little golden cradle with care to see that it has been perfectly cleaned and licked till it shines again; and then she must deposit in each a bluish egg, not much bigger than a pin's head.

There is a mystery about these eggs. All look alike in size and shape and color. Yet from some of them, worker bees are born, sexually impotent females dedicated from birth to death to fulfilling the labor necessary to the city's existence; from others, male drones emerge; and, on rare occasions when necessity arises, worker eggs are given special treatment by the nurse bees, and then produce young queens.

The ruling queen of the city knows exactly how many workers she will require, and how many drones. By a movement of a muscle she can control the future, and act her goddess rôle of ruling destiny. There shall be just so many males and no more. If food grows short, she may discontinue the birth of males altogether for a time. If her deific wisdom tells her that, in five or six weeks' time, flowers such as she has never seen will be in full bloom and giving their honey freely, then she swiftly increases the laying of worker eggs, and so provides a population ready for the summer's need. Do not suppose that this is a mere blind instinct, or that workers are produced in indiscriminate numbers all through the summer. There are only a few main honey flows —from the apple blossom, from the white clover, from the limes, and perhaps from the heather; local conditions may provide moderate minor crops; but there are time gaps between the flowering of the bee harvests, and in these time gaps the wise queen arranges that few bees shall attain maturity, whereas tens of thousands of young foragers mature at the beginning of each main honey crop. More than this, if a flower harvest fails through some trick of soil or climate, or if a prolonged rainy or very cold spell, useless for honey gathering, coincides with the main flowering of a favorite crop, a prudent and experienced queen will meet the emergency with a deliberately restricted population; though how she can prophesy, several weeks ahead, when she is laying the eggs, what weather or flowering will be like later in a world she only knows by hearsay, no one can tell. Godlike foreknowledge is hers, paid for in Heaven knows what silent horror in her more impetuous past, when, perhaps, she bore two or three thousand loved children each day at the false promise of a treacherous summer, only to see, later, all those who so implicitly trusted her and who were flesh of her very flesh, sent out uselessly to die in cold winds and smiting silver rain.

But this year her mysterious wisdom tells her that, in a few weeks' time, there will be placid and unshadowed sunshine, and fields creamy with dancing clover; so she lays her eggs at a rate of more than two every minute of the twenty-four hours, by day and by night, in the polished cells of wax. They are all worker eggs. Since last autumn she has laid no drone eggs, for the only purpose of the male in this city is to carry the fecundity that may one day have to be given to a new young queen. The ruling queen's foresight showed her that she would live through the winter and into summer again, so no drone would be required to mate a yet unborn princess; therefore, no males were created, and such drones as saw that earlier summer through were cast out to die, so that every particle of stored food should be preserved for those alone whose mission was to carry on the community life.

The goddess is gentle and patient with her children. She

does not rule them. If they decide that the time has come to swarm away to a new home, leaving a nucleus population behind to continue existence there, it is they, not she, on whom the responsibility for this desperate and dangerous upheaval falls. Sometimes she is reluctant to accompany them. They cannot live without her, and they force her to go with them, even so far as using physical violence to compel her to come. If they wish to extend the confines of their home, their engineers undertake the task without consulting the queen. If an intruder is to be warned off, or attacked, the decision lies with the grim sentries who form the city's regular army; the queen does not even know of it. Indeed, she is a fearless, unaggressive thing; she bears a royal sting, curved like a sultan's scimitar and not straight like her people's little daggers, but she disdains to use it, and may be picked up and handled quite safely, though the troops who guard her are of very different mind.

Like a true goddess, she dwells in a mystic seclusion of spirit. The others plan and worry, fight and work, gorge or starve; but she moves queenly-quiet, surrounded by those adoring maids, intent only upon the regulating of the population of the future, bearing three thousand children in a day, perhaps, graciously accepting the clearest honey because it builds the future, lovingly submitting to being washed and brushed so that she need never waste a moment from the paramount task of creation that must go on for ever until she dies. In her lifetime she may lay two million eggs and so give birth to two million children; in active periods she may lay more than twice her own weight daily of the little bluish-white eggs from which all those of her own kind whom she ever knows must spring.

As the summer advances she may raise the population of her city to over one hundred thousand, and this despite the loss by death of perhaps a thousand of her dear children each day. In the autumn she stops laying to allow the numbers to shrink perhaps to fifteen or twenty thousand; of these, all but a few thousand die during the winter; and then, with vigorous laying, she begins the cycle of life anew.

Once each year in the life of the queen there comes a ceremony of profound importance. In the golden city in the oak all the bees knew, though none had ever witnessed it, that the bringing in of the intoxicating crop of pale honey from the apple orchard had set in motion a strange sequence of events. Commotion which even affected the devoted young nurse-bees spread secretly in a contagion of quivering silvery wings, scurrying feet, jostling and head-turning and murmuration. Almost passionately economical of movement, the bees found themselves doing things without reason —hurrying feverishly among the combs, reaching with tremulous antennae, leaping from waxen wall to wall, obstructing entering honey-bearers who instantly became as excited as they. Throughout the humming thousands there grew a sort of coherent movement centering on the queen. Gradually all of those who were turned towards her where she stood, surrounded by her maids, on a central comb, ceased to struggle. They stood swaying slightly and similarly, glimmering in the faint light, pointing with their heads. Others swung themselves rapidly round so that they, also, could look. The change communicated itself as far as the outer combs. Even the sentries, dark and forbidding in the city gateways, turned and watched, never ceasing in their duties of examining every entering bee, yet contriving so to do it that they could stare inwards towards the distant center of the city. Presently, almost the whole population was pointing and swaying, and the murmuring and shivering of their wings grew loud.

Like a goddess receiving the worship of all living, the queen gently examined a group of waxen cradles a little larger than the rest. As she placed an egg tenderly in one of them, the song of adoration increased, and all the bees moved forward, crowding reverently—and then circled and flashed and broke and doubled away again as though a dark and shining mirror had shattered into a million pieces, and took up their work where they had laid it down.

But the excitement did not still. It rather increased; new vigor and a deeper song of happiness informed their tasks. It was as though, while they worked, they turned their heads continually to tell each other what had happened, and to steal another and another glance at the queen moving steadily among those larger cells.

The first drone egg that they had ever seen had been laid. The first drone egg of the year, the earnest of a new and portentous future. All these were females, but that cradle would soon hold a male. None had ever seen a male, yet their unsensuous nerves, condemned to a dim half-understanding, could rejoice and worship this mysterious creature, bred by choice and desire so that he, or one of his brothers, might perpetuate the race in the body of a princess yet unborn.

Unable to guess at his delights, they were ready to work for him, to care for him and keep him in luxury and idleness all his days, for this one purpose only; and when the autumn came again, they would know that his usefulness had ended, and would in worship sacrifice him and all his pampered brothers for the city's sake.

So they went about their tasks like people who have turned a new page in their history. Before them they could feel, though they could not define, the mists of a future they would never see shaping into dread and glorious events —the Royal Song, the frenzied decision to go out and seek adventure together in the unknown distances, the swarm dance, and an indomitable flight through the blue depths of some unborn summer day to establish a newer, more perfect home.

Tired workers returning from the fields with loads of honey or bags of shining pollen did not pause to unload their treasures, but joined the excited discussions among the groups of urgent bees. Nurses paused in their duties to gossip and conjecture, only to spin round with guilty starts and shames to the care of the impatient, furry babies who thrust their heads out into a new world, come what may.

And the queen-goddess, to whom more than to them all the laying of the first drone egg was significant, pursued her immortal way quietly as before. She alone knew that this first step might involve another, in the setting up of a royal cradle whose occupant would presently emerge eager and able to kill her royal mother should she delay her farewell from the city she had always ruled. She knew that one of a score of accidents might delay her departure, and that then she must submit to death at her princess daughter's will. She knew dimly that the swarming which could save her from that peril would bring a thousand others darkly in its train, not for herself alone but for the massed thousands of her children; and that if she set off unwisely, it might involve not only her following but also the city she was leaving in irretrievable ruin. She knew that everyone around her would be dead before any such day could dawn.

She knew also that she would see the world again, which she had seen only once for a few minutes soon after she was born. She would feel the hot sun again, see the flowers again, watch the leaves lift in the wind, smell ten thousand scents, dance down the vastness of the drowsy air on shimmering wings, know swift and unfettered movement, and glide playing through alternate light and shade. She would face peril and adventure and conquer them, give royal assent to the site of a fresh city and watch it grow, taste the glory of achievement and the sharp pang of fear.

As she walked the drone comb, placing eggs in this cell and that, her little maids looked at her lovingly and hurried to caress her. She was content; they wished to know no more.

CHAPTER SIX

The Bridge of Color

AFTER the laying of the first drone eggs the bees worked harder than ever. Dimly, they sensed the increasing tempo of life that was soon to include males bred to quicken a yet unborn queen, whose presence in the city would necessitate a mass emigration of more than half the population. To answer such a reduction of population at midsummer, faster and faster births were needed; and that meant more and more honey.

So they flew from the tree earlier in the morning, and stayed out working later in the evening; on warm days so late that the last were still drifting home in the velvet dusk.

For the first time they began to learn something of the new life in the fields and woods that takes over from the daytime creatures as soon as the sun sets. Only once or twice at the very height of the apple-blossom season had any of them been out of doors after sunset. Then a few hardy ones, straggling back to the oakwood with final loads of honey, had heard the bubbling melody of the nightingales, and the soft clicks of the tree-buds bursting their sheaths as more and more young leaves uncurled, and seen the pair of badgers who occupied the oakwood stirring abroad in the semi-darkness, hungry after their winter rest.

Now, many more creatures were active. Glowworms, holding high their lamps like Hero signaling to her lover; woodlarks singing vespers at a tremendous height in the evening sky, from which they could still see the sun; foxes on the move through the coverts; the first cockchafers, mad with joy at their release from winter underground, and out and about, knocking down everything in their clumsy way; curlews crying and skimming near the ground; everywhere the air and the earth were alive.

Enemies were about, too. The first wasps, voraciously fierce, lurked beneath leaves on the topmost twigs of hedges and trees, in the paths of bees coming tired and overladen through the night chill, which was already beginning to numb them. Just as the bee beat its way past, the wasp would leap out most precisely and bite the bee, while still in mid-air, on the back of the neck. If perfectly administered this bite would cause immediate and complete paralysis. As the bee began to fall with rigid wings, the wasp would catch it in its claws and jaws and bear it, living but quite helpless, back to its nest, there to lie for a day or two, able to see and feel but not to move, until the wasp-brood required fresh meat. At other times the wasps would be seen killing and carrying home plant lice, caterpillar pupae, flies, gnats and other living things, or scavenging for dead insect bodies; but they preferred to hunt, since it satisfied something essentially cruel deep down in them.

In the daytime now the bees spent much time fetching water from the stream for their brood. Except during main honeyflows this work kept them very busy.

To the bees, the stream through the wood was a living thing.

It flashed and gurgled through a channel fringed with mosses and ferns and purple loosestrife, which cast a dissolving pattern of shadows on its bright surface and reflected a sky more beautiful than the original, for the white cirrus clouds and expanses of varying blue were ruffled and glittering with the playful movements of the water.

But the bees felt a guarded neutrality towards this active monster. It gave them water; but it swallowed them sometimes, too.

They preferred their water sun-warmed and gathered it mainly from shallow puddles, where horses' hooves had sunk in the mud at the edge, or from stray splashes among the grass, where the sun smote warmly through the willows that bordered the stream. Each bee had her favorite drinking place, which showed her own individual outlook toward life.

There were the eager ones, always in a hurry, who could not wait to toy with puddles, but must hurl themselves on to the very edge of the vast sheet of crinkling silver. These bees were very irritated by playful river flies, which they darted angrily at but could never catch. Later, too, the mayflies, hovering and flitting and often deliberately tormenting, in their bold black-and-white, dancing through their single evening of life, infuriated the late water-carrying bees. Precariously balancing on a dipping twig, the bees swung their bodies rhythmically, staring possessively round at everything—the discreet, pale violets; the tiny shrimps peeping from beneath the muddy edges of large, flat stones; the stately bowing of the underwater weeds, the rippling V in the wake of a moorhen, and especially fiercely at the strong

shoulders and scarlet spots of a trout lounging carelessly by—
for trout have a dreadful propensity for curling upwards in
a sudden leap and swallowing a bee while the argent drops
from the splash have not yet fallen back into the stream from
which they came.

Older bees selected splashed stones, safely away from the
moving edge of the water, and sucked up delightful moisture
almost as warm as the perfumed air. Others would settle on
the branch of a May tree, where it dipped in the stream, and
crawl down it to the water's curling edge. This was dangerous. Many a bee had been swept suddenly off from the
treacherous dark bark, by some eddy of the surface, and
had gone down, turning and struggling, chilled and soggy
and ever feebler and darker and smaller, till the laughing,
careless river raced over her head and she took her last
glimpse of a sun-kissed world seen growing ever more remote
through the intensifying lens of deepening water.

Sometimes the drinking bees saw cattle come down clumsily to splash in the stream. The bees rose exasperatedly if
a muddy foot loomed too near, only to dart back again instantly the loutish juggernaut was out of the way. Sometimes
they would circle, whining viciously, near the cow's head.
It was a joke with them; they would no more have stung a
cow than a willow tree; but the monster dribbled in alarm
and stumbled hastily away stricken with bucolic amazement,
and probably sending up a new winged cohort as she went.

Sometimes, just now, as spring daily put on a more
gorgeous gown of color, the kingfisher, who flashed like a
neon sign up and down the river, would bring his family
for a lesson on to the pole that spanned the stream, marking
a farm boundary.

He would range them carefully along the pole, two feet above the water, and stand, invariably at the extreme end of the pole half in shadow of the bush into which it was stuck, with the sunbeams piercing over his shoulder down into the water like transfixed golden spears. Very beautiful, he was, with his incredibly sharp beak and graceful stance, and that plumage which legend says was gained while flying upwards from the hand of Noah—the hue of the sky upon his back, and the reflection of the setting sun flaming on his breast. And very still—and if the eight fledglings did not tense themselves as though they had seen the Gorgon's head, he would rush along the pole and peck wickedly, and be received with squeaks and screams of dismay, only to return again and cock his bead-bright eye to challenge the quiver of so much as another feather.

So they would sit, rigid as colored stones, perhaps for several minutes. The passing air did not seem to stir the down on the intent little necks. And then—*splash!*—Father Kingfisher would dive vertically into the water and vanish—perhaps the belief that his dried body would avert thunderbolts comes from this thunderbolt power, since it is said that two never fall in the same place.

Up he comes, vertically as he dropped, and appears so suddenly on the pole again that it is hard to believe that he has ever left it—save for the tiny, wriggling fish in his beak. Commotion explodes like a bombshell among the eight fledglings—they scutter, fight, screak, wave wild wings to regain lost footholds . . . but their flashing blue parent taps the head of the little fish twice on the pole, importantly, like a toastmaster calling for silence, and hurls it from him again into the water, where it floats listlessly on its side, slowly drifting beneath the pole.

The furore that began just now was Trappist compared with what follows. Every greedy little bird can see an enormous, a colossal, meal idling downstream—in what must look to them like a boundless ocean of tossing waves. They hurtle against each other, squall with rage; one actually runs right under the pole and up again between gluttony and terror. But the kingfisher is a Roman Father. Putting his head down and diverting that great thorn of a beak, he runs rapidly along the pole and plows them all off, screaming. Some make a wild flutter up and back again, shouting most unfilial abuse. One plumps flat on to the water and rises breathless like a tennis ball bouncing. One or two sideslip, wild balls of feathers, into the May tree. One alone makes a clumsy sideways dive after the fish, plainly thinking that Death might as well come to a full stomach. He grabs the minnow by the tail and hoists it with colossal effort into the air and staggeringly on to the bank. Seven fluffy forms like seven cannon balls arrive almost simultaneously. They are obviously Communists, believing that all is for all; but a thunderbolt in Toriest blue plows them apart once more, and the captor of the stunned little fish proceeds to put his life really in danger by attempting to swallow it whole. The others, gibbering and dancing with rage, are plowed away once and again; presently there is no fish, but a swollen, astounded-looking fledgling grossly proclaiming self-satisfaction and virtue rewarded.

The drinking bees see it all as they pulsate their shining bodies or stand poised with rigid wings before leaping into the air like ballet dancers; the changing life and beauty of the river, its tragedies and comedies numbering millions every day, are observed dispassionately and minutely, polarized according to the profits or perils that they bring to the golden city, and interesting for nothing else.

Not all the water-carrier bees go to the same drinking place. To some, the water seems sweeter further downstream. A few go as far as a mile from their city to gather the bright drops of life-giving fluid. The tongue of each, with its one hundred rows of little hairs, sweeps from side to side, gathering shining droplets in the hairs, while the jet eyes show infinitely tiny pictures of blue sky and rippled blue reflection in the stream, of tossing willow leaves and bending reeds and dot-like, passing, drifting weed.

Returning to the city, each water-carrier is subjected to a particular scrutiny, sometimes being gripped in scaly antennae and held still, or grasped menacingly in the jaws of the sentry. If there is no struggle, its hold is as light as the mouth of a spaniel on game; but any other answer save submission would be instantly fatal.

Strange creatures, these sentries, more sexless than the frigid worker bees, stronger than the biggest drone, more pitiless than the stream which chokes a drowning bee while laughing silvery at its struggles. They are females without mercy on even the downiest baby, which they would dismember with nothing more than fierce rejoicing at the economy of effort needed to sunder its tender limbs.

Promoted—or, perhaps, degraded—from among the thousands who go out to gather the sweetness from the flowers, their rôle changes from Love's messengers to Death's. Ugly and hairless and grim as public executioners, they stand at the city gates, rest rarely and then always alert to fly to their posts, and so exist until they die. There are only a dozen or so of them at a time; when one dies, another is appointed. The selection is made from among the fiercest of the field bees, those whose savage temper and naked torsos show them to be experienced fighters. Perhaps they have survived an unfinished duel with a wasp, coming suddenly from an accidental clash at the stream or in mid-air; its scythe-like jaws have mown the down from the future sentry's back, whose supple strength in avoiding the fatal blow marks it out for a new and grimmer career. Perhaps the worn, shining body has been polished by casual knocks because a fiercely urgent spirit informed it always. But the selection of the hairless bees as sentries is not chance; like an oiled wrestler, the sentry cannot easily be seized, the jaws of opponents slipping from scarred head and legs and body—and then comes the resistless parry that sends one more little consciousness out into the everlasting space.

Some say that sentries are condemned to their work because they have attempted to rob another bee colony, to gather honey by crime instead of industry. Though their fierce challenges are suffered by the rest of the population, there is always an air of loathing in the contact, which is shaken off immediately the business of examination is done.

The sentries do not care. They are loveless. They hate each other as bitterly as they hate those who legitimately pass in and out, and those trespassers on whom, in furious joy, they jump with murder announced in every thrilling fiber. Sometimes, when two rush together at an incomer, having reluctantly released her as innocent, they eye each other quivering with hate, and then fly fiendishly at each other, fasten avidly, and struggle whirring to the edge and drop, still venomously writhing, into the grass below. Some discipline greater than their rage tears them apart, and they leap up again to their deserted posts, ready with redoubled malice to turn their snapping jaws against a real enemy. They are like higher creatures; by hating, they hate more and more.

First to detach themselves from the drowsy warmth of the cluster at the cold fluting of dawn, they take up their posts long before the earliest water-gatherer is astir. Last to spring up on to the cluster at night, after the latest honey-drunk reveler has spun belatedly home, they never sleep, but merely slacken iron strength a little and hang watchful nearest the entrance to the city. Any strange sound or movement on the night air sends them bolting to the gates as if the invisible shears of Fate had clipped them off from the thick, warm mass of their people.

If, during day or night, an intruder comes too near the city, though he be as gentle as a nightingale or as huge as a man, the sentries run stiff-legged outside the gates on to the taking-off platform, fill their air sacs with a vicious whir of wings, point savage heads, and poise ready for a battle to death. They strike first and preferably at the eyes, and try to plant their stings there. Other bees may follow them out and sting casually here or there, but the sentries try to blind. Other bees sometimes insert the sting without injecting poison, but the sentries strike to hurt. Others sometimes screw themselves round and round so as to withdraw the sting intact; but the sentries force it in till it will go no farther, and then leap away from it, disemboweling themselves eagerly so as to leave the poison-bag pouring its last bitter drops into the wound that none shall be lost and not one tremor of pain be avoided.

Today, the sentries were more sullen and snarling than usual. There were continual brushes and scufflings. Incoming bees were seized roughly, and almost flung away through the gates into the oak. Though the law, which none may break, rules that no sentry shall ever be resisted, yet the way the incomers turned their heads was menacing. Precious balls of pollen that had taken tiring pains to gather were jerked out of the baskets and sent rolling away. Old bees who had given a lifetime's service were knocked over and thrust and kicked out of the way.

This ill-temper communicated itself swiftly to the city streets. There was shouldering and shoving and deliberate bumping. Young bees, pushing their heads through the lids of their cradles, were stamped on by horny feet, and withdrew, pitifully agitated that the world should be so cruel. Gentle nurses were flicked from their charges by the passing of foragers towards the honey vats.

Only the queen and her maids went entrancedly on their way, like creatures under a lovely spell of magic. These maids have brief service with their goddess; a day or two and they must move on to other tasks, replaced by more perfect younger virgins with eager tongues and gentle eyes.

The humming in the waxen city rose louder. There was distraction here far more fundamental than mere irritation at the churlish temper of the sentries. There was fear—panic fear.

The bees rushed to and fro in the golden streets. Workers came crowding in, many of them with half-loads, some with none at all. Their movements were jerky, terrified, sense-

less. They beat their heads against cells. Some dipped wildly
into open honey vats and began to fill themselves with loads
ready to carry away in case some frightful doom fell upon
the city and destroyed it.

The fanners at the entrance worked harder than they had
ever done in their lives. No matter what terrors befell, theirs
was a task of selfless duty and must go on. They dug their
claws into the wood, bowed their strong legs for better grip,
and flickered their wings too fast for the eye to follow. Disturbance in the city meant much more heat exuded from
frightened bodies, and more heat must be dispersed by a
steadier, stronger draught of cool air.

Cool air! The air outside was thickening, becoming hotter and more humid. It had a sour flavor. Instead of refresh-
ing, it brought vague fears and lassitude and enervating
timidity. More and more bees came mobbing in, exhausted,
though none of them now bore any sort of load. Familiar
trees nearby loomed unnaturally huge in a weird, reddish
light. Fluttering and palpitation and infirm despair seemed
to fill the atmosphere. The sky was purplish and crowded
down upon a cowering earth whose living things had vanished, and whose vegetation shrank. Though the air came
and went like fetid breath, there was a coldness behind it
as though Death walked.

Out of the infinite distance, racing at blinding speed
across the face of the universe, came a great hurricane
of silver spears of rain, hurled, it seemed, by an invading
army of demons. The rain pierced and tore through the
trees, with a great puff of hot wind behind.

Then, suddenly, a doom-crimson cloud burst like a rose,
and from its belly there rolled a growl of thunder echoing

away across the earth and out of sight. At the sound, the bees' perturbation was shocked into stupefaction. Where they had been foaming over the combs like black water, they stopped and crouched. So, when the world ends, might the multitudes crouch.

A flicker of light as from the heart of a sapphire painted the inside of the golden city a ghastly blue without shadows —and vanished, leaving everything black. Before the normal pale light returned, a bubbling caldron of thunder, in which earth was only a leaping speck of dust, occupied the universe. The stiff oak shuddered and the sky opened and closed; the city moved; the bees abased themselves, though their anger glowed in them and sharpened the cold air beaten through the streets by the rushing pinions of the storm. Outside, the rain throbbed intolerably, steadily gathering force.

Immediately, while the bees still seemed to wait permission to breathe again, the thunder went rolling away into the distant skies like a drunken giant, the clucking of the rain loosed and spent itself in a few last, huge drops, and a patch of sunlight flung down like a gold cloak at the foot of the tree, where every curve and surface glistened and a sudden, intolerable, faint sweetness rose from the sodden earth.

Then, silently, a rainbow threw a seven-colored scarf from end to end of Heaven. The foot of the rainbow discolored the ground twenty yards from the oak, and some reflection or evanescence from it became apparent in the city. The bees, reverently, yet in frantic haste, poured into the gateway and flooded like shimmering treacle on to the flat space of wood outside. The most fantastic thing was that they were silent. No bees hummed. No wings beat. They gathered there, crowding and staring at the stupendous bridge of color that reached from them into infinity. What could they see crossing that single span of ruby, flame, gold, emerald, sapphire, purple and amethyst?

Slowly, the vision faded. Patches of vivid blue appeared in the sky between slaty smudges of broken cloud. The bees flowed in through the city gates, and the sentries were subdued, guiding the runnels of crowding bodies mechanically, as though their minds were seeking truth out upon the bridge of color, and only tired shells of scaly black were left behind.

Inside the city the murmur of industry recommenced and grew. But there was restraint in it all the time until, when the long shadows of evening gathered, it sank to the faintest humming, the song of the night. The glory of the rainbow had done something to the bee multitudes. Their sense of color, so infinitely more intense than ours, perhaps makes the sight almost unbearable. The things of dust had looked upon the art of the immortal gods.

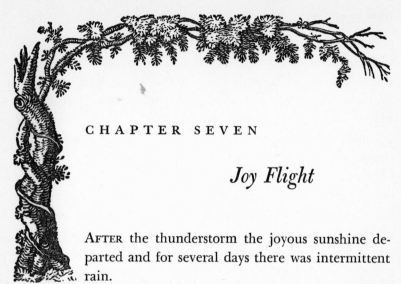

CHAPTER SEVEN

Joy Flight

AFTER the thunderstorm the joyous sunshine departed and for several days there was intermittent rain.

It flashed into the woodland from sullen clouds whose edges were intolerably sunlit. The earth was dark and subdued, but great patches of sky, wonderfully blue, shone between billowing continents of cumulus driven by a racing wind straight from the sea. Where the hills turned their faces to the light, up behind the wood, the tough heather clung more tightly to the earth as the gusts tugged at it; and bees foraging were forced to restrict their journeys, because the struggle against the wind and cold numbed them.

Many were forced down, overloaded, and sought shelter on the lee side of a stem where the sun struck fully, until their breathless bodies could face the turbulent air again. Sometimes the sun withdrew sullenly. Then the tired bee stood trying to gather strength by vigorously swinging its abdomen; and if this was not enough, or if another wild fluster of rain slapped the countryside, its clinging feet grew gradually looser, the jet of its eyes dulled, and though it perhaps clung there dreaming till the blown banners of stormy cloud streamed across the evening rose, there was a whirling fall at last through infinity to the depths where the ants waited to transmute death to the scarlet stuff of life.

Inside the city the bees crowded to watch raindrops shimmering by like fleeing multitudes. Each drop was almost as big as a bee, and their eyes could see the pearly shapes, each one perfect and translucent, striking the ground and splashing each into the form of a coronet with spikes, at the tip of which were round jewels glittering like diamonds, before all collapsed in silver streams and were swallowed by the avid earth. Some raindrops struck each other in mid-air and exploded into millions of brilliant fragments. Some, gliding off leaves, momentarily took new shapes like pieces of wrought silver glittering-new from the smith, or tiny twisted columns of moonshine from a temple in a fairy hill.

Only the strongest foragers went out in this weather, not because others would not have dared it, but because economy of life is the only way into the halls of the future. Inside the city, though the fanners worked never so desperately, a population swiftly swelling by a profusion of new births steadily raised the temperature in the overcrowded streets. These young bees were needed. In a few weeks the foam of white clover would be breaking over the green waves of the hayfields, and on the golden harvest of this sea the little fishers would depend for their means of life through the varying fortunes of another year.

This time, before a main honey flow, was the heyday of the docile little nursemaid bees. They had occupied the combs nearest the center of the city in the earlier spring, but now that the sun had sent lusty warmth into the colony, the queen had laid her eggs further and further out until part of almost every comb was occupied with eggs or brood in varying stages of development. Already workers were busy on the outermost combs of all, polishing and licking and cleaning the cells so that they should be ready to receive their sacred gift of life.

At the top of the combs was stored ripe honey, mostly capped with light-colored golden wax. This was food ready for use. Next were more vats, filled with uncapped honey, which still contained a fair proportion of water. This could not be sealed over until sufficient moisture had evaporated, in the heat of the city, to render the honey capable of indefinite storage without becoming rancid. A little lower on the combs were cells with dark wax cappings, into which pollen had been mixed so that the tops should be porous; inside these cells were hatching bees, which needed to breathe air from outside. Many patches of these cells stood out from the comb a little higher than the others, and they contained young drone males. Other cells, still open, displayed pearly-white babies in various stages of development from almost invisible tiny larvae up to rudimental creatures almost the size of bees, with heads and much of their bodily shape, but without the mystic gift of wings. Next these were cells capped over so that the wings might grow secretly away from impious eyes; and beyond these again, antennae reaching out to life, like seeking hands eagerly thrust through the breaking wax cappings, importuned grave destiny for happiness.

The baby bees, bewildered, but blindly confident that the world they could not see would be lovelier than their dreams, struggled with pitiful impatience to break their way out into life. Who knows what aeons it must seem to these tiny things that they have passed in silky veils of subconscious existence, slowly dying and painfully coming to throbbing life again as each worn-out shell is cast off, and each new metamorphosis begins yet another illimitable ocean of time, which must be crossed before a new stage can be made nearer to perfection. Who can tell how intolerably, and with what burning longing, they pass through the last moments, when they know themselves perfect, yet are divided from existence by a wafer of gold-leaf wax through which they can actually see dim shadows of reality passing to and fro, and smell the very texture of the woof of life, into whose pattern their scarlet thread is ready to be cast.

They grasp at the cell-capping from within, bite it through, plunge at the orifice, force their heads through and actually see, with marveling eyes as round as black opals, myriads of beings like themselves busy each with a different entrancing pursuit. They thrust with their shoulders in an agony to burst out and be free. They force a leg through the capping, and are held impotent, while priceless seconds pass that can never be lived again. Helpless either to emerge or draw back, they taste the color and movement and delight of occupation while they themselves are still as death. But gathering strength inspires a convulsive thrust; the wax cracks away; a milling scramble—and they are out, standing among a whole race like themselves (who thought themselves each in her solitary cell the only spark of life in a great void), poised on the brim of wide honey tubs, able to eat, able to move, able to communicate and be understood—able to fly.

They stagger, downy and clumsy, out of the way of intent workers who brush against them with marvelous carelessness and casualness—having exasperatedly seen such little egotists before. Perhaps they are knocked head over heels by the careless swing of a pollen sac. Then they pick themselves up and run madly somewhere, for life is not all it seemed in dreams, and has sharp edges and heavy antagonisms. They get knocked over again, and get used to it, and to the grumbling growls which accompany it.

Then hunger establishes a roaring claim. The sharp fragrance of new honey causes them to glance furtively left and right—dip a head into an open cell. . . . Perhaps they are sent flying, headfirst into it, for sticking their rumps out further than is conventional—and nothing in the bee city is more inviting than that! They struggle out, faces and whiskers dripping with glittering globules of gold, and frantically learn the next fine art in life—how to wash one's face. Ah, but this is intoxicating—this bumping, jumping, gormandizing career is *living!*

They sit down and begin to discover their bodies. Up till now these have been mere cases for feelings. Now they become articulate. Wings of virginal gossamer are drawn under legs provided with a stiff spike for cleaning them—they will need cleaning one day when they are smeared with pollen from the undiscovered world. Antennae smooth as velvet are painstakingly teased through a notch in the front legs, where eighty pigmy teeth caress what will be tangles on another day. The powerful pincers on the third pair of legs are opened and shut for the delight of stretching muscles that have never been used; the little bees do not know why they move these pincers, but soon there will be work for them

to do. Each feat is self-applauded by the delirium of sensa-
tion that follows successful achievement for the first time.

The long tongue whisks out and curls and touches waxen
walls and kisses its own feet playfully. All the thousand scents
that spell Home are savored one by one. The sound of the
fanners, the nursing-song of the brood-tenders, the wild
chorus of the honey-gatherers and pollen-bearers, the little
madrigals of the queen's gentle girls, the marching song of
the sentries, the triumphant swan-dirge of those who will
come back no more, the fondling whisper of the summer
breeze with all its perfumed messages, the blandishments of
dancing leaves, the distant songs of birds—these are the
symphony that welcomes bees at their birth. And they have
no chafing adolescence to curb them—they are born full-
fledged.

No one pays any attention to them in their fortunate new
freedom. They can wander all the combs at will, thrust en-
quiring heads into any cell, ask questions (which are never
answered) of the busy ones whose playtime has passed into
work. They can drop oafishly on to the back of people legitimately engrossed, or pop out and stare startlingly into the
faces of passers-by; they can eat like gluttons and sleep like
sloths and get in everybody's way, with no more than a
friendly cuff as quittance that is a delight to receive since
it proclaims the joy of notice and fellowship.

Like a magnet the broad bar of sunlight at the city gates
draws them all. But some timidity from the pains of birth
has not been finally cast, and though they advance upon the
light with hungry eyes, and smell it with challenging antennae, and stretch out quivering tongues to taste it, and
touch its warm nothingness with uplifted foot, they dare go

no further. This is the chrysalis again—the same dim vision of colors and sights and sounds and vast, unformed excitements somewhere out beyond, always beyond; it is what man feels when he imagines Heaven.

The nurse bees pay no attention to them now, these little sisters who will be nurses themselves after about twenty-four hours—the only playtime they will ever know. Nurses are fussy, important creatures, well knowing that the tongue that cleans the cradle rules the world, and deafens it, too, sometimes with day-old wisdoms that nobody heeds.

They have their duties, and they hope they know their places, which seem to be everywhere, and shrill are their voices when a dispute arises whether a polished cell shall be used for the honey that is now beginning to overcrowd the city, or whether that cell shall be preserved as a cradle. A cradle, of course, it becomes; the bee with a load of honey may be tired and right and logical, but the nurse with a load of importance feels herself the guardian of the future, the attendant upon destiny. Besides, she is fluent with the terrible, tireless fluency of the very young. So the honey-carrier goes elsewhere, the cell that glimmers like a new sovereign is scoured with furry brush and dustpan foot, a head is lifted confidently—and the gentle queen comes lovingly to place a magic spark of life in the very center of the beveled walls of the new cradle. The nurse examines it, with her head on one side, to reassure herself that eight hundred million years of queenly instinct have not suddenly gone astray. But no! the egg is precisely vertical upon its base, and all is well.

Tomorrow that egg will bend over towards the comb—but tomorrow the nursemaid will be gone, after concluding her week or so of this first duty, and will be hanging in the silent cluster that is feverishly producing new wax for more storage space for the invading tide of honey. Tomorrow, in her place, will be the baby who has just emerged, its little play-day swept away already from the life it had so ached to reach.

On the third day the egg will lie on the base of the cell, just about to produce its larva; the speck of life that has existed so far on the substance of the egg will push out towards a world where stouter food may be found. Then the nurse will elaborate infant-milk within her own salivary glands, and for four days she will keep the tiny creature that grows so fast contented and warmed. Whereat it will once more demand a change to braver diet; a mixture of semi-digested honey and pollen must be added to the food, and so, until the ninth day from laying, the nursemaid of the time will spend her hours running up and down stairs between the nursery and the pollen-filled combs near the gateway of the city—and still more abrupt and intent and dignified will she become, as befits one midwifing from the womb of Time.

On that mystic ninth day she will fill the cell with food and watch it sealed with a shining seal of wax and pollen no less inviolate than that seal set on a tomb in Palestine long ago, and, like it, to be burst asunder by new life. Twenty-two days from the laying of the egg, the young bee emerges into the waxen city, and the nurse of that day, who only yesterday perhaps was waving feeble signals to unknown passers-by to help her struggle forth from her own birth-shroud, today behaves as though she had done it all herself. But nurses are like that. . . .

And so, as the showery days continued, hordes and droves

of young bees drifted drunkenly down towards the city gates, and mobbed and milled there, getting in the way of the honey-carriers, who knocked them cheerfully head over heels a thousand times a day; for the warmth and the dampness were bringing up the nectar in the flowers in such quantity that wings would scarce beat or tongues wag fast enough to gather it. The velvety little monsters even dared to banter the tramping sentries, and were answered with a sardonic flick of a powerful shoulder that sent them reeling out of the fairway unhurt but very frightened indeed all the same. After the fashion of the very young, they jostled together, sympathized with each other, boasted frightfully, played pranks on each other and made passes at the sentries' backs, and crowded ever nearer to the delicious, the seductive bar of light that poured like a golden river through the city gates.

How they watched it! Sometimes, when the sun flashed out, it grew burning bright. Then, in cloud, it would become pale white. Presently, its luminosity would be shivered by the flickering of rain splashes—a phenomenon that never failed to startle the irreverent young bees to a statuesque awe that amused the sentries mightily, and made them stride to and fro curling their whiskers importantly and brushing their antennae together as men brush their hands who have concluded an important task.

And then, one steaming afternoon which looked just like any of those lambent, stormy afternoons, but which the bees somehow knew heralded a spell of unbroken sunshine to come, a knot of fieldworkers, tough and sinewy and ironical, spread swiftly through the multitude of young bees born in the last few days. This was more than the ordinary dis-

ciplinary bunting everyone had got used to. These bees
moved purposefully, and the youngsters, protesting, threatening, knocking one another over, found themselves irresistibly
swept towards the gates, from which the sentries stood back
scoffing with ironic mockery.

The workers, many of them fully loaded with pollen or
honey, formed a cordon behind the simmering pool of youth,
and at last it was being swept out like a black waterfall
helplessly over the far edge of the alighting ground outside
the gates, and dropping—as far as those gripping with their
claws and flinging back with their weight to avoid the same
doom could see—into nothingness.

But the pressure from behind was like destiny itself, and,
with a scutter of wings and a scratch of slipping feet, the last
few dozen youngsters were shot into the air. Hundreds had
already fallen headlong on to the leaves at the foot of the
tree, and raced panic-stricken whichever way they happened
to turn. Hundreds more clambered up grasses and plant
stems and even tree trunks with more energy than all that
which they had used in their short lives so far; but this led
to new desperation, because now they found themselves almost airborne, yet just as far as ever from the longed-for
security of a lovely city suddenly cut away from their touch
as if it had never been, and represented, if at all, by a dark
hole in a giant tree, and a few gleaming, quizzing eyes that
shone from its darkness.

All over the ground they rolled and crawled and scrambled, on top of each other, beneath each other, clinging
madly to each other for courage. Streams of them set off,
following leaders who knew nothing whatever, in various
directions, panting with fear lest they should not get some-

where in time for something. Some stuck all their claws into the earth and arched their backs, in deathly determination never to be driven from something that was, at least, solid and not like that awful emptiness through which they had just fallen.

But some, in falling, discovered that they had wings.

To say that they flew would be a libel, for they rocketed and slumped and sideslipped and lurched, cannoning into and knocking each other down to the ground, attempting to alight on each other in mid-air and clutch each other with a drowning grip, trying to fly backwards at the same time that they fought to fly forwards. But—they stayed airborne precariously, found that they could climb in this nothingness as well as fall through it, that a flick could avoid an obstacle as well as—and perhaps even instead of—driving one headlong into it.

First some, and then crowds of them, began a curious flight vertically up and down, with their heads all pointing towards the hole in the oak. Why, this was freedom, this was warmth, this was ecstasy! Who would walk—who would go crawling back into that old place—who would endure insult from mere footbound things . . .

The sun came beaming. They had never seen the sun, never felt the grandeur of its endearment. Their wings seemed to stretch till many of them thought that they were ten times natural length—and pride suffered many a fall thereby. They began to perform flying tricks, and to attempt some that no bee on earth could accomplish. They swelled—and all the while the shining, bantering eyes watched them from the city gates to which they swore they never would return.

Those on the ground, itching with hunger to emulate, began to vibrate their wings, found their air sacs filling—and suddenly sailed off into the air and became more extravagant than those who had been flying a whole two minutes. This was intolerable, so the latter flew at them and all upset together; but now it did not matter because they could fly up again at once—or even before!

The masterful sense of pattern which rules bees' lives sent first a handful of them and then more and more sporting into an aerial gavotte. Still all keeping their heads turned towards the city gates, they darted up and glided down, crossing and recrossing, flying sideways and diving and backing and bowing and flirting; and, as they went, their ragged, nervous humming changed to a song of concerted sheer delight in the loveliness of life.

They had never seen leaves before, or the wind stroking the grass. They did not know that there were trees or flowers or smells or clouds. God looked upon his handiwork piece by piece and found it good, but these young bees saw it all at once and could not express their enchantment except by concerted movement that filled the forest glade like a visible prayer.

For perhaps half an hour they swung up and down before the oak. Workers coming and going went philosophically round or swiftly through them. Finally, all but one or two were flying. Almost as one individual they tired and began pouring back through the golden gates into the city. The sentries dealt with them leniently, knocking them aside if they trespassed into narrow paths kept open for the workers, but doing it negligently only. The noise they made as they crowded in was deafening, each boasting and telling incredible tales of sights seen; and not one listening at all. Passing workers, invited to believe what could not even be seen in a five-mile flight, shrugged and hurried on.

The youngsters immediately went to their places beside the waxen cradles and commenced licking them, caring for the larvae, examining the eggs with their heads on one side, and piling food into cradles ready to be sealed, in a frenzy of conscious rectitude. They were not children, to idle their time away at the gates and get in people's way—they had the privilege of working at delightful tasks, and, indeed, dare not rest, for on them and them alone rested the whole responsibility for the future of the race. This egg, now—or this larva . . . was there ever a more beautiful larva than this? Of course there never was—nor one half as perfect. And that is what comes of having the right people to do the nursing—people who can *fly*.

On the ground outside, where the coolness of the evening was beginning to cling, a dozen or two derelicts from that joyous aerial voyage clung desperately to the tops of grasses. Some of them had never known what it was to fly. Perhaps they had been born lame, poor little things; they had struggled and beat their wings like the rest, but to them the air remained hostile, and the beating wings were like beating hands on an invisible prison wall. A few had flown too much, and were so tired that they would never fly again.

One of these, more ingenious than the rest, climbed with infinite fear and solicitude from one stem to another, and so on to the bark of the oak. Pausing more and more often in the growing cold, she struggled upwards on an endless journey. Many times she gave up hope, then forced herself upwards again. At last she turned over the lip of the alighting platform and thankfully edged towards the city gates.

A sentry ran out, seized her by her little waist, dragged her to the edge, and tossed her carelessly into the air. She did not even strike her wings on it to break her fall, but rolled down into the leaves and remained there, faintly moving.

The sentries stared down at the motionless forms on the grass tops. Theirs was a dispassionate task. Only the perfect, in this golden city, are allowed to survive. When the last chance was gone of any of those below trying to creep back to the warmth of the city, the sentries leapt one by one up on to the edges of the bee cluster and hung there. As night fell, creatures stirred among the leaves on the ground and began their butchers' work.

CHAPTER EIGHT

The Sculptors

FOR about a week after the joy flight the young bees were busy caring for the brood. They did not leave the city, except for very brief cleansing flights taking only a few moments, but devoted themselves with insatiable appetite to cleaning, warming, feeding and fondling, believing firmly that the last was as important as all the rest put together. For this is the life of a bee—to be born in a waxen cradle made from honey, to be caressed till old enough to give caresses, to feed from bounty freely given from the hearts of flowers to which she carries the seed of love, and to live and die in the unselfish service of her race.

At nights when all the workers were home from the fields, clinging together in warmth and comradeship, they would communicate to the nurses visions of the size and color of the flowers that were rioting now through the summer days. Or they would enlarge upon the excitement of discovering a new bush or a field just breaking into bloom—the smell of it like the very fragrance of dawn, the endless expanse of it flaming in the sunshine, the flavor of a new honey never before experienced. Gradually the nurses, too, became fevered with the yearning for these adventures and delights, as destiny bred in them the urges that would presently send them winging out to taste all the rest of life that lay between them and death. Honey-carrying was now approaching its height, as the first tight buds of white clover prepared to unfurl their feathery petals. Already, many hundreds of bees every day were failing to return to the hive; worn out with work after a comet-life of only five or six weeks, with no other memory but happiness and contented, useful industry, they crawled each to the top of her chosen pillar of summer grass, and waited quietly there for oblivion. Day by day those who had been born two weeks or more joyously answered the silent call of the fields, abandoned their work indoors, and sped out of the city like spirits at the beckoning of an enchanter.

Did they ever regret the tranquil days when furry babies reached out to them with helpless gestures of love? Did they remember the first few hours of utter irresponsibility, clumsily gormandizing in the honey vats? Or did the memories fade and vanish at the sight of the lifted faces of pansies, mignonette, forget-me-nots, bold strawberry blossom, sweet may blushing red and white, flaunting charlock, dainty sainfoin, and fashionable, chic French honeysuckle?

Before they might venture out and sip the honeyed mouths of flowers in loving promiscuity there was, however, a ceremony of initiation to be passed.

From seven to ten days after starting nursing duties, first one and then another and another of the glossy adolescents, having reached the acme of strength and beauty, swung up in lovely, curving leaps from the nursery combs to the new civic space which had been cut by toiling bee engineers from the softening wood at the heart of the oak. Guided by some mysterious sense of far future need, generation after generation of bees had canalized a runlet of moisture from the outer trunk inwards, to soften the iron core of the old tree in the place where, today, excavations were going on to make ready to extend the city's waxen streets.

In the space already cleared, perhaps as large as a man's fist, a cluster of young bees was already hanging. These had all been nursemaids yesterday. Today their lofty scorn of children's work was evident in the deeper song they sang, and in the aura of isolation that was rigidly respected by workers, nurses, sentries, even by tumbling infants and by the queen's majesty herself. No one approached them save the time-served nurses who, each with a peculiar grace and dignity, sprang upwards in winged victory to attach herself to those undergoing the mystery. The lines of laborers and cutters and designers who toiled further down at enlarging the new space were careful to circuit the shining black glimmering cluster, hanging like a bunch of grapes from the roof of the oaken cavern. The queen's maids, with loving touches, gently guided their adored to and fro about the last completed comb, half filled now with eggs and tiny larvae, in such a way that she should not approach their sisters in their seclusion.

For these young ones, putting forth for the first time in their lives the very uttermost of their strength, were submitting themselves to an ordeal so exhausting and so vital that not even royalty must cast a shadow there. In the high summer this exorcism is the gateway through which all must pass to the freedom of winged life in the fields.

These were the wax-makers.

Before leaving the combs and springing on to the festoon of clinging bodies the initiates had filled themselves with choicest honeys. To make one pound of wax, from six to twelve or even fifteen pounds of honey must be first consumed; the ceremonial feast precedes the novice's initiation, and on former temperance, exercise and developed resolution depends the capacity now to feast voluptuously to gain strength for a supreme trial. Nor may it be approached lightly, for the essay is most dangerous; those who have not rigorously prepared themselves will stagger away from it dying.

The sacred hymn of the sculptors takes rhythm and depth as the festooned bees interlock with one another in a grip that not the most passionate climax shall break. At first, it is a song of praise—an imperious proclamation of delight because workers alone, not sacred drones nor yet more sacred queen, have ventral organs for producing the golden wax without which there would be no city, no store of food or cradle for the young, no race . . . no race . . . no race.

For the first time in life the young bees are obsessed with a convulsive desire to move the ventral plates that guard the wax pockets and the delicate, highly sensitive membranes which secrete the treasure they are to produce. Urged by the stimulation of the song and of their closeness, they cluster tighter and yet more tight at the center of the black ball of bodies, while on the outer edges newcomers festoon and embrace.

Hour after hour the initiation song moves through its throbbing stanzas, and the bees press tighter and tighter upon each other till the temperature of the cluster rises far above that of the rest of the city, reaching 95 degrees or more. The strain on each striving body is deathly, but it is inspired and increased by the gratification of achievement and by some dim foreknowledge that only through this agonizing bliss lies the way to halcyon days.

From heat and intimacy the ventral plates of each clinging bee rise and fall in tiny, rhythmic waves throughout the whole cluster. When the first bees swept upwards to seize the key positions of the pattern on the oaken roof, the sun outside was almost at its meridian. As the hymn of initiation gathers strength so the sun declines. The sweet breath of afternoon sways warmly through the city, and then the drowsiness of summer evening, and the transplendency of moonshine. Every other bee is clinging in the safety of the clustered combs, but in their ravishment of beatitude the sculptors are equally unconscious of day and night. The earlier unsynchronized wavelets of communal delight are running now with the strength of a spring tide as myriads of ventral plates rise and fall like the beating of a single heart intoxicated at the approach of enchantment. All through the silver silence of the night they clung there entranced, and then embraced still closer yet to challenge the stealing chill of the dawn. Time stood still for them; this twenty-four hours was lived so blessedly in that dim, intimate Arcadia that it partook of the nature of eternity, without beginning or end.

Next day, when the sun stood again at its highest over the buttercup fields of the cloth of gold, the first reflections of that outer-world magic became manifest in the singing throng. With a visible ripple of emotion that shuddered through the locked communicants, the bees nearest the roof gave birth to tiny scales of translucent topaz which oozed with thrill upon thrill into the wax pockets guarded by the ventral plates.

So thin and light these wax scales were that one hundred of them weigh less than a single kernel of wheat. Ejected liquid into the pockets, the wax solidified there, and the assuaged bees relaxed their embraces and deepened the note of their triumphant anthem to a sighing of lovely exhaustion.

As the new theme spread slowly to those below, and they, too, shared the satisfaction, the bees near the roof called from the depths of their spent strength the last reserves that were essential for the consummation of their happy ceremonial. Each one began exhaustedly to remove the wax scales from the pockets by means of the hairs on the legs, and then to pass them forward from foot to foot until they could be transferred to the mandible jaws. Contentedly, the work of softening and preparing the walls of the future went on until, at last, the eight tiny offerings of lucid wax could be built on to the symmetrical patterning now beginning to cover the roof of the excavation in a long oval divided by a central line.

Gradually the sculptors shaped their masterpiece from the living gold they had themselves created. As the bees crawled, utterly spent, from the top of the cluster, master builders moved down to perfect the shaping of the comb. First its vertical midrib was lovingly fashioned; then from this, back to back on each side, sprang the cells, sloping slightly down and back so that when they should be used for honey it would not run out. Each six-sided cell was a miracle of perfect workmanship and exactitude, twenty-eight of them to the square inch, smoothed and polished like yellow marble.

As the top of the comb took its form, and the last touches were given to the cells there, the initiates lower down achieved their culmination, while those lower still remained entranced awaiting it, and at the bottom of the cluster those who had but a moment before been unconsidered nurses leapt joyously up to dedicate themselves for the ceremony.

So, hour by hour, the comb grew down from the roof, faultlessly parallel with the last previous comb; and all the while the engineers toiled unceasingly to cut out space for yet another comb of the future. Presently the novitiates clung in their desperate embrace below two or three inches of shining new comb, and on this, hordes of nurses swept and polished before the approach of the queen and her circle of maids. Very soon the uppermost cells held precious eggs, and life itself stirred foetal wings upon the walls of gold.

Each initiate, having taken her guerdon of the newest honey, and refreshed herself, and rested, walked forward joyously to receive the freedom of the world, and sped on gleaming, sun-splashed wings out towards the far horizon. This loveliness had been dearly earned; now the gates of beauty were unlocked and flung wide.

And, presently, some of the wax-makers carried their gift to another part of the city. On the central comb, furthest from all dangers, warmest against every invading chill, a group of master builders were singing the Royal Song.

Passers-by in the golden streets paused in adoration before running on, carrying with them a magical excitement that was like nothing any had ever known before. It stirred their feathered shoulders and possessed them with dim visions of further fields, remembered from ten thousand generations back and golden with asphodel. It cried adven-

ture on shimmering wings, seeking truth from the veiled face
of the unknown.

This cleared space sacredly prepared, this great base leaping to springing walls—none had ever seen, and the master
builders who shaped it had never known the like of it. The
perfect curve, downward-hung from the comb like a
sharpened gold thimble, with walls lovingly chased with
cabalistic runes, was a temple built out of race-memory
alone. Solidly constructed of virgin wax, joining the comb
only at its base and uncontaminated by common touch, it
had an air of dedication.

Nor did it grow alone. Six of them, each cunningly placed
to avoid any catastrophe that might overwhelm another,
hung majestic as the days went by; and with each one the
excitement in the city simmered and grew. The young bees,
allowed in their foolishness everywhere but here, stood in
groups as near as they dared come, and watched in wonder.
Toilers from the fields, no matter how tired or near to
death, never failed to pay quiet homage by turning their
heads in adoration as they passed by. The sentries never
approached, going out of their way to join the nightly cluster
at a distant point.

Only the queen, in wisdom and sorrow, came to inspect
the work—and she advanced alone, for her little maids drew
back timidly, following her with longing eyes from the
nearest cells.

Not even their goddess had seen a queen cell before
within her immemorial memory, though she had emerged
from one at the beginning of all that misty past; but before
she had assuaged her royal rage at rivalry and established

herself in splendid and dreadful isolation to rule the world, those who had followed in her train had cut down every temple and trampled out the walls.

Where a goddess had been born no lesser thing may profane that holy place.

again the disconcerted sculptors came bowing; but in answer
to some silent message the royal maids closed up in a pal-
pitating barrier of sweet dignity, walling them off from the
presence; they flustered in pitiful anxiety, but majesty went
on her way serene, and they were left waving frantic antennae, uncomfortable and ridiculous.

Perhaps the queen knew that enough had. been done to
appease the high gods in whose hands the city was but a
grain of dust. Perhaps she saw that this cell would produce
a weakling without inspiration. Perhaps, divinity as she was,
some streak of inconsistency still informed her sex, and she
would not go to this place because she would not, let come
what may.

The sculptors bustled away mopping their heads with
trembling forelegs. They stopped gangs of workers and took
breathless counsel; they stared at the festoons of wax-makers
as though their occupation was gone; they went at last to
those who would always, and about all things, give plentiful
advice—the nurses.

The nurses were struck dumb. They were paralyzed. They
stared from their informants to the distant empty temple as
though they had never heard such a thing in their lives, even
though these had already numbered two or three whole days
apiece! They regarded royalty's divine unconsciousness
darkly. Finally, an inspiration flew among them like a contagion. They darted, paused, raised protesting antennae,
shoved, stared, shivered and gasped. The masons' former excitement was superseded by something like a frenzy. They instantly created ten times more commotion than ten times as
many nurses. This froze the nurses into contemptuous amazement. They could scarcely believe their eyes. That a simple

suggestion—the putting into words of the only thing in all the world that could possibly solve the difficulty, a thing which anyone in his senses would have realized for himself (as the nurses had)—should cause all this ridiculous fuss. . . .

They turned their backs upon the sculptors, and these divinely inspired few who alone could erect the great temples, stared furtively at each other in shame. The nurses took no further notice of them. They began instead an overwhelming and feverish argument. Which of these eggs, which nurse's own most perfect, wonderful and lovely larva-child, should be given the accolade? Which one of these half-conscious thousands should be borne away in triumph to become—divine?

This egg is perfect. My furry child is quite incomparable. That head there—the celestial brow alone makes it predestinate. The other, with the eager, splendid movement—surely it is haloed already with an unearthly light?

Down in the gateway the fanners brace themselves for redoubled work. Something profound is happening up there in that seething mob. The heat from within redoubles, and to the fanners it means only one thing—their wings must beat faster and faster yet; their leader steadily increases the silver rhythm. As for the sentries, they poise ready to charge—perhaps a wasp is there—and though they soon know that it is nothing they can alter, they regard the jammed crowds watchfully and gloomily.

The nurses have decided!

An egg is lifted from a worker cell by its nurse whom events have changed into a priestess. As she bears this seed of destiny triumphantly towards the empty temple, thousands of nurses and workers, drones and newly emerged

neophytes march in concourse around her, humming an anthem that has never been heard in the city before, one which
springs into the consciousness of those who have never heard
it, as tribute to the little god whose foetus they accompany
to its divine altar. It is laid lovingly within, carefully bal-
anced on its end, and all that multitude backs away as one,
bowing and singing, while the master sculptors regain their
place and dignity upon the walls.

Not yet can the temples be sealed. Under the tutelage of
the dark abbess who carried the egg here, a singing band of
young priestesses advances and prepares to anoint the altar
with the strangest of all the wild ambrosias of the bee world.
Royal jelly defies all attempts at analysis. No one knows
from what it is made or how it is prepared. Fed to the new
inhabitant of this cell, or to any ordinary worker larva not
more than three days old, this magic substance transmutes
the little neuter into a queen; but only if it be placed within
a proper queen cell with authentic cabalistic marks upon the
walls. (When a tiny quantity is mixed with the food of sterile
rats in a laboratory, they become potent and normal breeders
within a few days; one day we may learn how to borrow from
the bee something which will drive the gray curse of sterility
from human homes.)

Devoted guardians of the immortal flame of royal life that
lay now upon the altar, the solemn band of priestesses tended
and warmed and kept it safe, while the master sculptors
raised the solid temple walls still higher. Then came the day
when that which was being born must be sealed in magic
silence, to attain, in solitude and privacy, perfection and the
loveliness of wings. Solemnly, the priestesses went in mystical
procession to the pollen cells, which bore perhaps fifty

pounds of the fairy dust each year, and brought back each her single grain of precious spice. These cells were like storehouses of jewels—some white, some blue, some palest green or deepest scarlet flashing grain upon grain in richest profusion. But only pollen of the purest sunny gold could be employed to cover a princess. Some believe it to be one pollen, others another, but the color is always the same. To the priestesses singing their song of dedication came wax-makers bearing virgin tribute, passing it to the master sculptors first, who scrutinized and fondled it and gave it devoutly to the guardians of the shrine. Mixing wax and pollen, they spun for the sarcophagus a golden lid, and having laid it gently in place above the sleeping thing within the temple, so cunningly furnished with a banquet of royal jelly, the priestesses passed chanting out into the flower-strewn fields. For them alone, the initiation ceremony of wax-making was waived; they had purchased the dear loveliness of the summer world another way.

Mysteriously aloof, all six of the golden temples now stood sealed. Within them, sleeping princesses stirred, turned, passed through timeless dreams of unknown colors and forgotten aeons and incomprehensible shapes. Presently, first one and then the others began to spin the silken veils within which they withdrew themselves to die, and burst forth reincarnate, and die and tremor back to life again. In the golden dimness of each sealed temple, larva magically changed to nymph and nymph to perfect queen, during eight illimitable days and nights of silence and growth, in which intelligence was coming to its dawn.

All this time, the blind excitement that had come to the city when the first queen cell was begun, grew and spread.

It was especially apparent in the drones. Big, dark and
bustling, clumsy and opinionated, they struggled into and
out of honey cells, knocked workers over, bustled past snarling sentries, fell over dandelions and grasses, trundled back
again, cocked their heads knowingly at the silent golden
temples, and incontinently fell headfirst into the honey
vats once more, charging themselves with food now so that
the lusty future should be well served.

But it was not only the drones who were affected. The
field workers, dazzled and dreaming, profoundly stirred
(none could tell why), abandoned their tasks, hundred after
hundred, and spent the sunny hours crawling and shoving
and gossiping about the city gates. At first, there were big
knots and groups of them, at whom the sentries rushed with
savage energy. But soon these groups coagulated into a
stirring mass that surged upon the oak tree; and at night
thousands of them clung in a great black ball outside the
gates, humming faintly like a multitude talking beneath its
breath. The sentries could do nothing. They could not drive
them off, or even keep roads clear through them. Bees
coming and going had to climb painfully over the backs of
the gossipers. And, as the days passed, the mob grew ever
bigger and moved more eagerly.

Inside the city, the queen still went her quiet way, though
now she was working harder than she had ever done in all
her almost immortal life. Selflessly, she was giving children,
three thousand or more each day, to populate this home of
hers after she had left it for ever. There would be a period
after she had gone and before the new young queen could
start to lay, during which no eggs would be placed in the
cells, though bee life would be dwindling tragically away

among the workers in the fields. So she prepared for that by an increased fecundity. Life must go on!

Then came the day when the master masons approached the first of the golden temples they had built. It had been sealed for seven days. How did they know how to count seven days, or that the virgin princess was stirring, now, in impotent supplication? Gently and carefully, they thinned the waxen lid till it was no more than a transparent wafer. Then, prostrating themselves, they retired backwards; and it seemed that the city held its breath.

The masons approached the queen. She looked at them sorrowfully, but this time the circle of her little maids did not protect her. The masons came as arrogantly as prophets, and communicated to their goddess that she must break the spell that had held her here in this city generation after generation back beyond time and legend; she who had only once seen the sun must come forth once more beneath its warm caress. The city was overfull. Within hours, there would be another queen. One half the population—more than half—would flee with her down the scented summer afternoon to find a newer home. She must come with them . . . MUST!

Their goddess looked at them sorrowfully. As they approached her, hustled her divine form, tried to drive her through the streets in a silver mist of faery-beating wings, the wild crescendo of excitement was broken, like the snapping of a cord, by a sudden outcry of dismay from the gates.

Rain had begun to fall. Not fierce rain, but gentle summer drift, misting the trees and jeweling the meadow flowers each with its own diamond. The rain fell persistently and steadily, but so softly that not even the throbbing mob of bees outside the city were driven in by it. They remained there, glistening and moving and discussing.

At news of the rain, the milling round the queen ceased. All fell back awed and abashed, and her maids crept timidly to her, fondled and tidied her where she had been so rudely brushed, smoothed her lovely wings, and tried humbly to placate her sweet dignity by offerings of honey. They had never doubted her wisdom, and behold! it was manifest. The swarm could not risk a flight in steady rain.

The master masons, falling over themselves to repair lese majesty, sped up to the temple where the perfect young queen lay awaiting her hour. Already, it was almost midday. Before evening, she would have thrust through the golden seal and out into the world awaiting her rule. But now that rain had delayed the departure of the swarm, that life so preciously prepared must never come to reality, lest princess and queen should fatally dispute their royalty. While other bees crowding in multitude on the nearby combs averted their eyes, the masons cut away the lid of the sarcophagus, reached inside, grasped the perfect thing that lay there, and tore it out into the profaning light. It moved slightly, and at that sign they seized it fiercely in their jaws, ripping its tender flesh apart . . .

When the horrid deed was done, they bore the corpse between them down the golden ways, and as they came the bees drew swiftly aside so as not to be touched. They carried the dead princess through the gates, and round the edge of the mob gathered there. The whispering rain played a tiny dirge for one born to be queen, who died before her time; and two of the bearers swung up the broken body and glided away with it through the weeping air to the city's graveyard by the river.

Afternoon declined to evening, and evening changed to night, and still the city seethed. All night long, and while the sun climbed the sky next day, the impatient humming went on and on, gathering in power. Then again, shortly before midday, the rain having ceased with the dawn and an ardent sun claiming the whole earth, the masons once more approached the queen.

This time, she met them mildly, and they fell back before her; in an instant, it seemed that they accompanied where she led.

As she passed very slowly along the streets of her home for the last time, as it were blessing all who stayed there, with a maternal and divine beatitude, the workers thronging outside the gates began to leap into the air thousand by thousand. The sentries were knocked head over heels and over again.

Through and through the city, a hundred thousand bees crouched as if at the signal of an invisible baton—then burst into motion and chorus. The wild and gathering tension of the past week found frantic outlet. Twenty thousand of them dropped from the combs like a storm of enormous rain, and began to pour out of the gates. These and the ones already outside had filled their honey sacs from the combs so that each bee carried a three days' ration. Thousands left in the golden streets now plunged their heads madly into the honey vats and began to fill themselves so as to accompany the others.

The city of peace and infinitely ordered labor becomes one wild confusion. Bees charge one another, leap up and

down, pour to and fro, and rush headlong out of the gates
like a mountain torrent of dark water. Forty thousand of
them are already in the air outside the city, shooting over
each other's backs and cavorting beneath each other's bellies,
swirling round and round as if about an invisible Maypole,
while others are pouring over the oak like so much treacle.
Sentries and guards and workers coming from the fields with
huge loads of pollen or honey are swept into the melée,
and even the most hairless, hard-bitten warriors whizz their
wings and kick up their tiny feet in the maddest of all
Arcadian dances.

Turning and always re-turning their heads towards the
city, they commence an extraordinary mid-air dance. Round
and round they go, with a glorious deep hum that provides
Nature's own music, as though Pan himself were playing it.
Perhaps he is there invisibly among them with goat's foot
and curling beard. Perhaps the pilot Thamus, commanded
by a mighty voice to proclaim, on that day when Jesus
Christ was born, that Pan is dead, meant that his uncanny
power was taken from men only; for anyone who has seen
bees swarm knows very well that Pan is there.

Inside the city, the queen approaches the gates. She fears
the light, poor little goddess; it is so immeasurably long
since last she went into the world. But the workers whirl
and maze around her till first her maids and then herself
become intoxicated with the frantic measure. For one
moment she hesitates in the entrance, but a group of dancers
swings against her and she finds herself suddenly unfolding
the wings that have been meekly crossed for years.

She is on the wing, flying more strongly than them all, as
the sunlight and sweetness of the summer day possess her,

more lovely by ten thousand times than everything her adoring maids have told. Her eyes drink in a thousand colors, a million wondrous forms, her body basks in sunshine and the scents of unknown flowers.

She turns away from the city, across the oakwood towards the river meadows. Seventy thousand bees surround her in mid-air, joyously pouring and rolling along as though enclosed in a gigantic barrel, round and round and over and under her, weaving a close and lovely pattern as they fly to meet adventure. Rapturously jubilant, they hurtle along with a joyous roar; and after a little while, attracted by the pinky softness of a May tree, in full bloom like a pillar of flame, the queen darts into its perfumed depths. Closer and closer round the twig on which she has alighted, the bees whirl in their ceremonial dance, more and more and more settling on it and gathering lovingly about their goddess, reassuring her by their numbers against all the perils of the world. Closer and closer they cling, in an inverted cone, till at last all are tightly clustered.

Away from these, fast as bullets, ping strong-winged veteran scouts, seeking a site for a new home. They travel miles, some of them, peering into hedges and clambering boldly within black crevices of trees, and each comes back to the cluster to report. The master masons, on whose judgment depends the safety of the new streets that are to be erected, listen gravely, and debate this and that possibility. Presently a scout returns with a tale of a perfectly dry, sheltered site inside the battlemented tower of the village church. There are no mice there—very vital, this!—and the crumbling stone the Saxons laid can be bitten out when

more space is needed. The masons wave their whiskers importantly; and are pleased to approve.

Thousand after thousand, the bees leap into the warm
air once more. The queen lingers a little, taking passionate
farewell of the lovely tree. The bees wait, rioting happily
in the sky. Presently their goddess joins them, circles with
them all round that mass of pink and round again, and
then sets off towards the church.

Swinging away sixty feet above the meadows where the
first clover is beginning to break, they close their ranks
against the edge of the old tower whose bells clanged when
Duke William's soldiers came pouring past from Hastings.
On the stone, outside what will be the gates of the new
city, the first bees are already landing, clinging with spread
legs and deliberately opening the Nassenoff glands which
give off the scent by which the colonials announce official
acceptance of a new home. Groups of bee dancers take place
upwind from them, and perform a whirling-winged measure
to create a steady air-flow driving that sharp scent outwards,
that all may realize that here life begins anew.

As the queen runs into the entrance, surrounded by her
happy people, the hum of the fanning dancers takes on a
new note of deep, entranced content.

CHAPTER TEN

Bee's Wedding

HALF an hour after the swarm had emerged, there was no sign outside the city gates that an exodus had taken place involving more than half its total population.

New sentries had been appointed and were standing guard as dark and stubborn as each successive regiment had been since the days when dinosaurs might have been numbered among their foes. Zealous young field workers, who had spread their wings in sunny freedom within the last two or three days, and had sped dutifully out to the first opening clover rather than stay and gossip about the city, were coming in with sun-splashed wings, bearing loads of the richest honey of all the year. They raced through the half-empty streets that had been so thronged, with no emotion other than delight that now the ways were free from loiterers, and that less time need be spent before another ecstatic leap into the white softness of a great clover head. Young bees still thrust foolish faces through the golden doors that had sealed them away from life, stared round, and accepted the streets as they found them, believing all things good. The nurses redoubled their energies, more sure than ever that on them rested all responsibility for the race's future. Most of the drones, with their propensity for furious effort at the wrong time, had missed the swarm by plunging waist-deep in honey vats the moment the final excitement began, and then paying such oafish attention to their stomachs that they neither heard nor saw anything more for half an hour. They would all have gone, otherwise, for wherever commotion was, they delighted to add to it; but Nature, needing them at home, had endowed them with one overmastering instinct—that of diving headfirst into a food tub in response to every agitation but one.

Two great gaps in the city consciousness existed. The queen was gone, who had been here in every legend since the first foundations of the golden walls were laid, she who had led her people here out of the vague unknown, generation after generation back. So people might feel if suddenly everyone on earth disbelieved in divinity. And not a single wax-maker was at work.

For the wax-makers had suddenly leapt from their places and forced their way first of the outpouring multitude through the city gates, to lead the swarm. Some old wisdom guided them. Before any other step could be taken in the new city, these must plot and mark out the lines for the walls, houses, cradles and food stores. They must work as they had never worked before, completing, perhaps, six or eight whole new combs within a single week. Not half of them would ever win the promised freedom of the fields and skies—most would crawl from the shining new city into the darkness of death, worn out with endeavor to furnish living space for the rest of the swarm and the generations that would follow, so soon as their goddess had cradles in which to place her eggs. If some of them had stayed behind, or if any, having gone, had worked more slowly so as to enjoy the rest of life in the sunshine and the flowers, the whole swarm might have perished in some bluster of autumn rain; or the queen might not then have had time to renew the race strongly enough to face the winter. So every wax-maker went with the swarm, flawlessly exulting in that last infinitely joyous flight, and then settling down to work herself willingly to death.

In the golden city in the oak the eldest nurses, so soon as they had seen sufficient of their little charges mature to replace them, headed straight out into the whitening fields of clover. Not for them the triumphant initiation from washing, cleaning and warming into the rapt embrace of a thousand sisters, the lovely trance that brought to living strength a physical power that marks the unfledged from those who may use their wings. Like children changed by magic to adults, they knew no youth. Instead, they must work harder and die sooner than any they had known. The exodus, carrying three days' honey load, had gravely depleted the city's food stores at the moment when more babies than ever before were being born—so many of them gluttonous and workless drones! There was no goddess now to tell whether, perhaps, rain might not suddenly make all outdoor work impossible and persist until every trace of nectar had vanished from the clover fields and only autumn remained.

So comb-building was stopped for the year, the first sad sign that life was not an everlasting summer. Small groups of older nurses, selected for the task because of special strength and eagerness, still produced wax required to seal the cells of ripened honey, and, later, when another queen reigned, the cradles of another generation. But all the rest who could be spared poured out into the fields, and labored there from soon after sunrise until the sun had disappeared. And here, too, the divine wisdom of their goddess who was gone from them was manifest. For she had so timed her departure that a dwindling of nursing duties, due to the stoppage of egg laying at her departure, coincided with the bursting of a white flame of clover across miles of green-velvet fields; and so the greatest possible number of nectar-gatherers could fly out to repair the losses in honey that the city had suffered when the swarm departed; and so, too, in her new home, the first anxious week or two, at first with only carried rations, was spent at that time of all the year when nectar was nearest at hand and most bounteously plentiful, and could be most swiftly poured into the store-houses that were frantically being built.

In the old city in the oak, though there was no queen, five of the golden temples still stood inviolate in their cleared forecourts. A mysterious silence enfolded them. Passing bees looked at them with awe. What was happening there, inside the golden walls on which the runes crawled blackly? Deep among the silken veils within, what godlike breath was stirring, and from where?

So, perhaps, the disciples waited for the stone to roll away from another tomb.

One temple had been destroyed. That from which the perfect queen had been dragged to her death, before she had even tasted the life she must have dreamed of so poignantly. After the swarm had gone, new self-appointed sculptors had cut away every trace of what had stood there; among the crowding cells they left a naked place.

The same new sculptors anxiously watched the remaining temples. Then came a day when, trembling with fear and reverence, they approached one of them, and started to thin the golden seal of royalty. No goddess was here to watch with benign eyes; what they did now, they must do alone, little, frightened people fumbling and stumbling in the outer courts of a blazing and unknown Heaven with extinction for all their race if they came too soon, or too late.

That night, a summer night of murmurs and moths and black and moonlit seas, suddenly above the steady drone of the night-fanners thrilled a new sound.

A little sound and shrill, like the blowing of a fairy horn, urgent and imperious. A shiver of dread ran up and down the streets. The wings of the fanners fluttered and quickened. The silence that followed was dark as the moment that follows a lightning flash.

The sound came again, more strongly, piercing the heart of the oak like a splintering dagger of glass. From under the royal seal in the oldest temple could be plainly heard, following that tiny piping, a stirring as of wings unfolding, a breath as of a spirit passing, and an elfin touching, forcing and scratching as of something trying to be free.

From end to end of the city, every other sound died. Motionless in the milky glimmer of moonlight, thousands of bees waited entranced. There was no fanning, no humming, no movement in the cohorts of wings, no glint or shadow in the glitter of all those eyes. Then, cut in a perfect circle, the lid that had closed the golden temple slowly rose, with its seals burst.

Divinely conscious of her beauty, with shimmering wings folded, a shining goddess emerged out of the immortal past into the immortal future.

A cloud passed over the moon, and the city was in darkness. When the silver light returned, the goddess was no longer there. She had vanished among the combs. Withdrawing herself into an obscure corner, she plunged her head into a honey cell and drank deep as a murderer who seeks to inflame himself to perform his horrid deed.

Having eaten, she flexed her muscles boldly; and then calmly took a waxen wall of a honey cell in her mouth and tore it from its place. The honey crawled away in the shadows like clotting blood. Not ten minutes had elapsed from her stepping out into life before she ran swiftly and suddenly up one of the golden streets, across the forecourt of a temple, and stood there, head raised, uttering again that shrill and challenging piping that had struck the city into silence.

From this temple, and from two others, came a fainter answer, infinitely little and pitiful—the sobbing of sleeping princesses imprisoned in their castles of gold, but imprisoned still tighter in silken webs of destiny from which they would never now come forth alive.

The answers to her mortal proclamation inspired the virgin goddess with a terrible calm. Proudly, she cut away the seal and raised the lid of the first waxen coffin. Inside, pale and perfect, lay her own lovely sister, mystically gowned in her shining shroud. She was alive; her eyes, wide open, watched her own destruction. The goddess stooped over her, and began coldly to draw away the silk whose warmth meant life, whose lack spelled death.

She worked steadily, watched by thousands in the moonlit streets. Skein after skein of silk was pitilessly unwound. Then, while her people crouched and the very air grew cold, she reached within, tore off her living sister's head, stepped back, held it Medusa-like on high to turn all on-lookers to stone, then cast that exquisite mask from her, and moved towards the next of the temples.

This, too, she desecrated, breaking into it, beginning to strip off the silken veils, and then, deciding that the work was too tedious, she tore down more of the wall to expose the tranced body of the nymph within. She observed its per-fections in the white moonlight with an appraising eye that sought the loveliest and most tender place in which to strike the fatal blow; then turned about and reached with the projecting, scimitar-like curve of her sting. She made several motions in different directions, quite leisurely select-ing the fatal spot, then struck her poisoned weapon lightly into the faintly shrinking flesh. She lifted herself round to unfasten the barbs, sheathed the blade, and moved on to the next golden dome.

Again, a temple was profaned. This time, the goddess drew out the corpse of a princess just emerging from her nymphal shell. She laid it down indifferently in the cleared forecourt, and passed on. From the next, she lifted out a royal pupa not yet formed. The pitiful thing rolled off the comb and went spinning down into everlasting darkness. Presently, languidly, the virgin goddess turned away from the last broken temple, and banqueted alone, drinking deep, but only to allay exhaustion—for the gods may not forget.

Behind her, moving in the shadows, edged the new master sculptors. As soon as she had opened a temple and done her ghastly regicide, and moved on, these ghouls finished the work, hastily cutting down the splendid walls, casting away the pieces, secretly removing the sacked body to the river graveyard, and leveling the temple site. Before dawn, but for six scars like protesting mouths sewn up, there was no trace of what had been.

But still, though a goddess walked among them once more, the crowds in the golden streets withheld their worship. Perhaps they were too agitated at what they had been forced to see. They drew aside where that slim, remorseless figure passed, so as not to touch her golden beauty. They offered her no food and tendered no caresses when she cleaned from herself the marks of what she had done. Nor did she notice them. She walked the golden streets, where thousands shrank back to open the way, as though she had discovered an unpeopled city. She explored its furthest confines, unresting and unhurrying, while drones and workers, sculptors and sentries, nurses and even the irreverent newborn, avoided her divinity.

The day passed, and the night, and another and another and another. Still the city held its breath, waiting some profound event. Still, the goddess was veiled in strange aloofness, mystically private among forty thousand of her people. None served her or attended her or approached. Hour after hour unsleeping, she passed along the familiar streets of gold, scrutinized the fortifications at the gates, criticized the lines of the newest combs which stood empty and deserted since the exodus, observed the damp runnel that the water-engineers had led to rot out the heart of the oak, estimated the swift-shrinking areas of brood and the expanding fields of stored honey.

No satyr drone pursued this virginal Diana born of the

stuff of moonlight. Pampered and cosseted and fed, they
bustled about the city, but their bold, black opal eyes turned
aside when she passed, because their mortal flesh shrank
before that which seemed unearthly. Towards the end, she
looked at them in calm and cold appraisement, judging the
sturdy bulk of each, the strength of wing and lift of head
and poise and stance and mien; and they stood as if turned
to stone. But after she had passed, each one, as though
hypnotized, slowly turned himself towards the city gates,
and walked there blindly; for when the gods reveal themselves, they burn the eyes.

And so, at last, while the earth lay drowsing in the sun's
embrace, the crowds in the city's streets pressed back, once
more allowing the virgin goddess way. She passed swiftly,
as if flying on a cloud; her hour had come; so winged Leda's
swan down all the heights from Heaven to earth. Like a
spirit, she passed through the usual busy throng at the gates;
her downward rush had filled her tracheae and still further
lightened that divine form; passing like a sunbeam through
the sunlight she had never seen, she spread her wings and
gave her body to the air.

Swiftly noting every tiny thing that marked her citadel
and its environs, so that she might find it again, and dipping
in a great arc as if in obeisance to the immemorial tradition
to which she must now make glorious submission, she sailed
over the heads of the group of transfixed drones, who had
remained immobile since taking up their places outside the
city gates. And, as she passed, the fairy piping that had
heralded her birth broke out anew, on a deeper note, as
from a reed with its heart torn out.

The wings rose on the drones' shoulders, and with shining

eyes, each with thirteen thousand burning facets, they stared at the virgin movements of an unveiled goddess. And then, as if to seek safety again in the place from which her divine spirit had descended, the little winged thing sped Heaven-wards with the drones in wild pursuit.

Up they went, faster and faster, with the world shrinking away below like a falling star. Wildly exulting, she beat the perfumed air and climbed straight towards the sun; and behind her on tireless pinions the drones followed a blind-ing beauty that none might look upon and live.

The pace never slackened; but first one and then another of the pursuers broke his heart, turned over and plummeted down to dusty death. One hundred set out, and presently, while the goddess mounted still, more than a mile over the crawling earth, there were but ten . . . five . . . one. So Nature mysteriously ordained that intercourse with divinity should be granted only to the most worthy, and that not one should live to speak of her unveiling, or of the sacra-ment whereby life came, welcomed once more by that small, Pan-piping cadence.

Nor yet would any future legend tell whether the incan-descent dust overmastered the living flame at last, and beat high above her on vainglorious wings, and struck hawk-like—to discover nothing but a shrinking virgin who could strive no more to reach the azure gates behind which the gods dwell. Or whether, instead, she stooped pityingly and gave divinely what mortal never could command.

Folding their wings about each other, brother and goddess sister locked in a searing flame of rose in the Elysian blue, and hurtled earthwards over and over while he throbbed out his life. The lambency of that divine maidenhead consumed his spirit, as it always does, and as she fell, she cast away his spent body down the gulf of the air. Like Icarus flying drunk with glory into the very heart of the sun, passion burned his wings away, but the spirit that had served the air unwavering as an altar flame did not fall, but rushed on in triumph across the sunlit, silent vastness of the universe with all its singing stars, into that happiness whose dim foreknowledge had comforted him always during his puny life on earth, and which enveloped him now in joy and glory ineffable and everlasting.

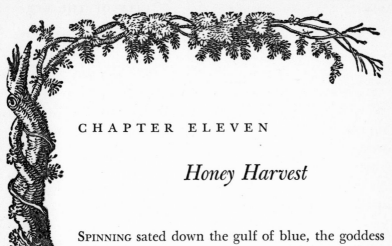

CHAPTER ELEVEN

Honey Harvest

SPINNING sated down the gulf of blue, the goddess presently identified the hill, the wood, the individual oak, and dropped exhausted on the platform outside the city gates.

The mysterious exaltation that had borne her to the heights of Heaven, was gone. Stored within her body, and at her full command, were twenty-five million spermatozoa; she who had stooped to mortal love was still divine, and could, by the movement of a muscle, control the future. All her eggs would be the same, but now she could impregnate more than a million workers, bear drones when she would, and bring to birth from her own body, if she chose, hundred upon hundred of goddesses like herself. With these powers came responsibilities; if she prophesied the weather falsely, or bore too many or too few children for the season, they and she would die, and the thread of community life stretching back far beyond man's history on earth would be cut short for ever.

As she crouched amidst the dregs of passion, looking steadfastly into the far distant future that she must shape, the sentries at the gates stiffened and raised their antennae for the first and last time in their lives in the royal salute. At that sign, a great rejoicing burst out like a song from end to end of the city, none knowing why. All work was stopped, and through the streets the myriad citizens swayed like clamoring crowds on holiday, dancing here and there and everywhere. Workers and nurses near the gates poured suddenly out and surrounded their divinity like one risen from the dead. They swept up to her singing; with infinite gentleness they raised her to their shoulders and bore her triumphantly into her paeaning city. Masses swept along before to proclaim her, and other masses followed in glorious jubilee.

So she was borne to the very center of the place, and set down triumphantly, when all fell back, leaving round her a little space walled by eager eyes. The goddess turned with gentle imperiousness, and signed first to one and then another and another to come forward. They obeyed with timid happiness, and the acclamations redoubled as they lovingly began to tend and caress her. They stroked the velvet gown of hair until it shone, kissed the silver wings that were folded now perhaps for ever, and fondled and petted her as though a thousand blessings came to them from every touch. With pretty concern, they sped from honey cell to honey cell, determined only to accept the best of all; and then bowed their heads humbly while proffering the amber liquid on delicate tongues.

The goddess surrendered herself thankfully to their care. She needed smoothing and cleaning and food and comforting; she must gather her strength from the deeps resolutely to put away the call of the sunshine and the spaces of the

sky, the appealing faces of flowers, the longing for color
and the undying itch of lust. What had been done once must
never be done again. What had been was memory; what
must be was work.

Unappalled, she looked into the future. All these, who
surrounded her, singing, must die. Generation after generation must be born of her, and all must die, leaving her, their
creator, forever alone. Huge perils would loom ahead, the
lives of thousands of her children would have to be squan-
dered to avert them, the city would be besieged, the summer itself would die and she must watch the icy fingers of
the cold destroy her offspring, and must create more and
more for that same purpose of destruction; some portent of
snow chilled her with a dim vision of a white and merciless
world. It would pass; summers would come again, and fade,
and die; only she would go on and on, omnipotent and all-
seeing, suffering the agonies of all, and never daring to seek
oblivion in death.

Was there regret for that brief, sunny mating—for the
drone, fatherless himself, the product of an unimpregnated
egg, who would now become the father of countless thousands through her body that had given him death as well as
love? He was fatherless, yet his sons would father an endless
race numerous as the grains of sand on the seashore; he,
her own brother, victor of a hundred brothers she had
killed, had sown within her womb the seed of immortality,
and without him the race would have become extinct.

As day followed summer day, the dwindling population
of the city grew again. With endless polished and empty
cradles inviting her, the new goddess gave herself unspar-
ingly to fecundity; soon more than two thousand of her

children every day came crowding from the combs to pass through successive stages and hurry out into the fragrant fields. She bore no sons; drones would not be needed again this year, and somehow she who had never known a winter was conscious of what she must do to prepare against it. There were still some drones in the city; they had been out of doors when she had led their brothers up to death, or some of them had not then been born. They went importantly about the streets, or sped out to revel in nearby flowers, happy, fussy, never dreaming of the fatal shadow that nights already beginning to lengthen were casting over their idle lives.

The clover harvest this year was bountiful. It whitened the hillside like manna, and massed ever thicker as the ground sloped towards the village. In the uncut hay meadows, it grew long-stemmed, swinging its dainty heads among the clashing grasses; behind the whirring mowing machine, it sprang up afresh in the night, starring the ground like sunlit snow. Haymakers—gnarled men, and brown girls, and children in daisy chains, and somnolent, contented dogs—heard the drowsy hum of the bee hordes thrusting their tireless way into that foam of fragrant white, and paused to mop their faces and stare up into the deep blue, and sniff the redolent air, and say contentedly that this was real midsummer.

Each bee, flying from the city to gather a load of nectar, visited more than one hundred clover blooms before it turned back towards the gates. That load would equal about one-third of a drop. In the nectar was from fifty to eighty per cent of water, according to the flowers from which it was collected, and to the varying dampness of the atmosphere. So much water had to be evaporated from the nectar before it had passed through the various processes necessary to produce honey that would safely store, that the weight of the nectar exceeded that of the final honey fourfold.

Yet the city must gather five hundred pounds of honey, between April and September, as a minimum on which race life can safely go on; four hundred pounds or more to support the bees day by day, and to store sufficient to last them through the darker months, about eighty pounds to feed the brood, and ten or fifteen pounds to produce new wax. Five hundred pounds of honey has to be collected, one-third of a drop of nectar at a time, each drop coming from the nectaries of three hundred flowers.

The bee darts from the city gates and travels to a particular "beat" which she has established as her own. She plans her routes methodically, passing swiftly over areas already being quartered by other workers, and drops on to a clover head at the edge of her chosen territory. From there she moves steadily to and fro, examining each flower, instantly refusing those not yet freeing their nectar, or those which have been visited or have passed their prime. Usually, she travels in an arc so as to fill her honey sac as near the city as possible, and thus have the shortest journey back. Wherever she may be then, no matter how she may have wandered in her search, she returns in a beeline absolutely straight to the city gates, runs inside, deposits her load in a cell either empty or containing that particular kind of honey (since varieties are never mixed), and goes out once more. On the comb, patches of cells are reserved each for its own kind of honey.

The nectar gathered from the flower becomes honey, the

cane sugar changing to grape sugar in the honey sac of the bee. From this sac, the load is expressed by the use of certain muscles, and thus it can be filled into the honey cell. The minerals and aromatic oils from which the flowers distill such sweetness give to honey those ambrosial flavors which caused the ancients to believe them drops spilled from the drinking horns of the high gods.

From the time when the pink buds break on the fruit trees in the spring, to the first dusty days when the white clover ceases to blow, is barely three months; and in this brief season of sunshine and showers, the bees must gather most of their sustenance for a whole year. Fruit blossom, dandelion, hawthorn, beans, clover, charlock and lime yield generous honey harvests; but when the greenish-gold blossom of the lime trees has faded, except for a little nectar from the blackberry trailers along the hedges, the willow herb, perhaps, the heather, and finally the tough old ivy, there is nothing more to cause excitement till the gold stars of the crocuses in the grass and the tiny florets of gooseberry promise the splendor of the apple blossom once again. The twelve weeks or so that end soon after midsummer day are the bees' time of destiny.

They go out to meet them with a will. But not all the wisdom of their queen, not the most giant efforts of every little worker in the city, can always appease the gods of the high summer days. A period of drought reduces to a pitiful trickle the flow of the nectar in the flowers; and the bees must search mile after weary mile to try to gather enough for their little loads. Chill summer nights mean that the nectar remains cold-bound until perhaps late on the following afternoon. Violent rain may beat the flowers down and draggle them. Hour after hour, on many a day of sunshine, the bees must loiter idly at home, though the meadows and hedges are bright with flowers, because absence of rain and dew has retarded the nectar secretions; and then a storm breaks and dashes the swaying, painted chalices shattered to the sodden earth.

But at the time of the clover, the bees in the city suffered from none of these troubles or fears. Splendid heat, softened at intervals of a day or two by the gentlest rain which was never strong enough to confine them within doors, drenched the crowding white blossoms with nectar. The briefest summer nights seemed all too long, as the workers impatiently clustered about the combs that hung heavy now with more than a hundred pounds of stored honey. The vivid fragrance of this honey, combining the lovely perfume of a million flowers with a sharper aroma reminiscent of as many breathless adventures in gathering it, pervaded the whole of the city and was clearly perceptible for some distance around the oak tree, especially at night. At the first touch of rosy-fingered dawn, they were out again in hundreds; soon the hundreds increased to thousands and tens of thousands journeying tirelessly to and fro, steeped in the happiness that the main honey harvest brings.

Even the sentries, though this was the very acme of their heaviest duty, and none of them lived for many weeks because of the strain of racing up to every bee of the crowding thousands and checking it as it entered, lost their moroseness for a week or two, and challenged friendlily, and helped occasionally to hoist up a dropped lump of pollen into place again on the carrier's leg.

The nurses redoubled their endeavors, young bees were

born—many thousands every day, and so full did the rows
of cells become that, at one time, there was a hasty confer-
ence whether or not to start comb-building once more. The
elder nurses proffered their services most eagerly, the masons
fussed up to the queen's majesty, but no more combs were
built. Already, the days were declining; the utmost strength
of all must be economized and employed to bring in the
last sweet drop of clover honey; labor dare not be diverted
at such a time, and laying was already beginning to dwindle,
guided by magic foreknowledge of the autumn gales to come.

And yet, outside, there ruled high summer that seemed as
if it would never end. The grass grew lush, waving and
shimmering across the boundless earth to meet the sky; the
drowsy glare of the sun lighted ten thousand trees like green
torches; behind rose the blue magic of the hills into a
profounder blue of the triumphant sky. Over acre after
acre of the river meadows, the air was stupefied with the
humming of the bees as they rose and sank to the whiteness
of the clover, urgently shoved aside the feathery petals,
poised with flickering tongue, jumped lightly to the next
swaying blossom, beat up a foot or two into the air just for
the incandescent joy of seeing illimitable loveliness, glided
down again, and presently flew heavily back towards the
wood, murmurously content.

Not all the nectar-gatherers worked in the clover fields.
Where the wind drove the sleeping spirits of the clouds in
shadowy fleets across the crests of the green wheat, groups
of bees, like silken-sailed shallops, floated towards the happy
isles where patches of charlock blazed. There they sank
entranced in a golden dream, gathering the sweetest nectar
of all the world.

Some of them, returning with loads of this thick honey too heavy for them to bear, fell victims to a strange mischance. As they approached the oak, a playful breath of scented summer wind sent them staggering. Several managed to reach the gates. Others, completely tired out, went gliding heavily to the ground at the foot of the tree.

Ants awaited them there. Before each bee, a fierce ant stationed itself, and stared pitilessly into her eyes. The bee remained motionless as a stone. Soon, some magic in the blank, black gaze of the ant's minute eyes began to act on the bee's consciousness. Unable to stir wing or foot, its mouth slowly opened and its tongue came out as reluctantly as if it were being dragged by invisible silver strings. The long black tongue uncurled and stretched out—and lo! on its tip was a drop of honey taken from the store in the sac, that store already dedicated to the use of the bees' city.

The ant advanced. The hypnotized bee stood rigid with extended tongue. The ant put out its own tongue and lifted all the honey it could carry from the bee's tongue-tip; and then turned and hurried away. Very gradually, the bee seemed to emerge from a weird dream. It withdrew its tongue, hesitated, then leapt into the air and hurried shame-faced into the city to deposit the remainder of its load. All day long, the ants waited under the tree; and so they do each summer, wherever bees live, tiny middlemen of the insect world, reaping where they have not sowed and gathering where they have not strawed.

Inside the city, the fanners were reinforced to their maximum strength, driving sometimes as much as a pound of water from the cells and out of the gates in order to perfect each pound of sealed honey. On the combs, hundreds of thousands of bees passed and repassed, bringing honey, caring for the brood, and sealing the cells of stores, as they ripened, with golden lids of wax. For all from man down to the tiniest insects, harvest time is a period of rejoicing; and up and down the golden combs went an unending harvest dance of nearly half a million tiny feet lifted by flashing wings.

Happiness was at its full. Summertime was at its zenith, with golden days, and dreaming, perfumed nights. Through all those gleaming thousands of little bodies poured the wild elixir of midsummer madness and untainted joy.

All save one. With eyes like black pearls that reflected all the dim and moving shadows of the future and the past, the queen watched summer unreturning diminishing down a corridor of days strewn with dying flowers.

CHAPTER TWELVE

Drone Day

SHAKESPEARE wrote of "The lazy, yawning drone";
yet in the bees' city the drones were astir as early
as anyone. Broader in head and body than either
queen or workers, heavier with bigger and more powerful
wings, they are innocent and inoffensive, possessing no stings,
and never using their jaws either in attack or defense. There
are no pollen baskets on their legs, and their tongues are
too short for serious work in the gathering of honey. Not
born until May and June, few are raised after July, and
seldom indeed are any allowed to live to the end of September.

There is something appropriate in this, that bodies created
for love alone should dwell in everlasting summer, freed
from everything but play, and gifted with vision unequaled
by any other living thing to glory in every detail of color and
form in that little sunlit eternity before perhaps a soaring
death at passion's climax in a hyacinth Heaven. Thirteen
thousand hexagonal lenses pointing in almost every direction give to each eye an infinite range and power. Life
must seem very beautiful to them.

One of them, glossy and sturdy and young, leapt from
comb to comb soon after dawn on a day at the height
of the honey harvest. He was amusing himself by tasting
various honeys from the cells, with the critical severity of an
amateur. He shared with human virtuosos a contempt for
everything of which there was a quantity; no matter how
perfect its quality, too much of it offended his refinement.
Not for him apple-blossom honey, or dandelion, or rich
new clover of this vintage year. He curled his tongue elegantly about a trace of pale hazel honey—it was too sweet.
This gorse, then, with the tang of the south wind in it?
Thin; definitely thin; and one must consider texture as well
as flavor in so grave a matter as this. Honey from a dark
poppy's heart, sleepy with velvet dreams . . . delicious, but
cloying at this hour in the morning—though admittedly almost perfect for the million-tinted eve. Wood violets gave
this, bright and golden clear; yet the experienced palate de-
tects a lack of boldness, a shadowy loss of fullness in the flavor; a woman's tipple, but hardly full-bodied enough for true
perfection. And this, from patches of forget-me-not down
by the river's edge? Ha! Here is the authentic bouquet—
but where is the aroma? Have you ever known an exquisite
woman with a common mind?

And this lambent spirit of the mignonette? He stands
with legs set firmly apart and eyes staring into infinity where
stranger colors, clearer forms and flawless passions are. As
he sips this perfect honey once again, he sees a city of coral
and fire with seafoam curtains and starlight stairs, set amidst
hills of shimmering pearl where a goddess drowsing on cloth
of gold faces the rose-red dawn.

He passes, this shining sybarite, able to resist the temptation to plunge headfirst into the magic cell of mignonette honey only by remembering in time that gluttony would dull the sharp edge of his appetite for ten thousand delights which wait submissively under the sunshine outside the gates, ready to do him pleasure.

The sun is shining strongly over a world of blue and gold, and he swaggers past the sentries and leaps fifty feet high into the scented warmth of it, his wings beating three hundred times in each second for the very joy of living. His humming song is louder than that of any worker as he spins deliriously up the sky and watches the oakwood dwindle and the shining horizon unfold to display to him an ever-wider and lovelier earth. From that empyrean, he observes fifty thousand workers from his own city, busy in the clover gathering honey for him, and a million others from bee cities elsewhere mingling and crossing, speeding in all directions like little bullets in a fairy barrage, rising and sinking above the swaying clover heads.

This crystallizes in his mind the plan for an adventure. He turns towards the distant village, and goes off at twenty miles an hour, singing at the top of his voice, towards a cluster of beehives behind a clipped hedge in the vicarage garden. Gliding down at a tremendous pace, he alights amidst a throng of workers rushing in and out of the entrance to one of the hives. Boldly, he strides up to the sentries, shoves them aside, and enters the place. For drones bear a mystic pass admitting them to any city—though their sisters or even their queen would be killed instantly if they attempted the same liberty.

This was delightful, to explore new streets, rub shoulders with a strange people, stare in bachelor doubt at the faces

of the babies and think privately that too much fuss altogether was made of the wretched little things, sate an infinite
capacity for wonder by idly watching other people work at
new walls, engineering projects, and the sealing of brimming
store-tubs of honey. Even to push importantly towards a
vat that was just going to be closed, and taste a little of it
so as to give benign approval that it really was ready for
corking, and then bustle off leaving shrill protests behind
because now the cell would have to be brimmed anew. A
soupçon of honey here, a scurry over to see what the crowd
was gathering for there, a bold appraisal of the shapely body
of the queen herself and a flirted whisker at her maids, and
then a staggering progress down unfamiliar and exciting
streets and into the sunshine once more, only to find with
delight that it was hotter and more fragrant than ever.

A whisk up into the air, clumsily upsetting an alighting
worker who rolled over and over on the platform and down
into the grass—but these little accidents will happen! The
drone, heavier and with bigger wings, recovered his balance
in mid-air, climbed up and up for the delightful fatigue of
climbing, glided down and down for the sweet rush of the
cool air to brush out his velvet jacket . . . and found himself circling the church tower, where bells were clashing a
salute to midday.

A million things of interest here—the shapes of lichen
pores, the angular movements of insects, the color of the sky
over the shoulder of gray stone . . . and, glory be, a worker
swinging home with two bright bags of pollen and entering
a crevice near the top of the tower. Curiosity pervading his
being like a delightful flame, the drone hurried to the place;
found a foot-worn passageway, bumbled down it to the ex-

treme discomfiture of half a dozen workers racing out, who
had to clamber up the walls to avoid his jolly rush, and
found himself at the gates of a city that smelt somehow
vaguely familiar.

The sentries made a satiric pass at him and let him by.
Oh, here was fun—a place half-built, with infinite opportunity to criticize the angles of the rising walls, the quality
of the half-finished honey vats, the dust that workers too
busy with other tasks had not yet thoroughly cleared up
for the day. And this haunting, reminiscent smell and scene?

Of course! These were the colonists—the emigrants of the
air. And here was a fellow "out from home" who could and
would tell these colonials what was authentic and what was
not. And how the folks 'way back would open their eyes
to hear what was happening in this place divided from them
by a waste of cloudy seas.

He stood on the fortifications of the gate and craned his
neck to get a better view. He jumped the infant walls like
any Remus, and was patronizing, approving, dissatisfied in
turn. Tired workers were triumphantly unloading the first
drops of thyme honey which he tasted condescendingly and
unasked; he became transfixed in a vision of limitless purple plains, to the extreme inconvenience of the workers, who
unceremoniously bunted him out of the way and got on
with their job. He picked himself up and dusted and combed
himself in no wise abashed, though the energy thus dissi-
pated required another sip of that imperial Tokay, which
had to be nipped up a trifle incontinently while a worker's
back was turned. Then he hopped away down the golden
street and out into the now definitely drowsy air of an eternal
afternoon.

Languidly, using the sixty-foot altitude of his take-off with the most amazing lazy skill, he floated across the meadows into a hazel copse. The very earth gave out sweet breath under this masterful sun; not a leaf moved, not a bird sang or an insect hummed, and the drone, with a sudden powerful beat of wings, hurled himself on to a leaf at the extreme tip of a slender hazel wand. Under the impact, the wand swung out in a splendid arc, and slowly back again, to and fro and to and fro for ever, while the drone soared dreamily with it and tried to remember a shadowy race instinct about the sea, and failed, and was content.

A velvety Vanessa butterfly came down a sunbeam and dropped on a nearby leaf, folding and unfolding its great wings to be admired. The blue eyes in its wings and the blue of the cloudless sky exactly matched. Faintly in the shining bark of the hazel appeared a distorted image of the butterfly, which prinked and flirted saucily in love with its own reflection, and then, with the softest whir and daintiest bow went gliding on its pleasured way.

The drone gazed omnipotently on the whole woodland to see what else should amuse him. Twenty yards away, perfectly immobile, sat an old cuckoo, shaded into the background of twigs and leaves, and a little way from him were two more. Three cuckoos in company made the drone stare, though actually these birds often travel together after midsummer. Then he became aware of a tiny flurry in an adjacent bush, beating its way towards the cuckoos. Then another, further away, and suddenly the whole sleeping woodland awoke in a savage twittering and a rushing of wings and a pushing about of leaves and an emanation of anger and envy.

The cuckoos hopped up through the branches and took the air like a squadron of hawks; and behind them fluffed and flustered and squawked a score of small birds of several different breeds up and in pursuit. The long, pointed wings of the fugitives quite easily outdistanced the mob of smaller fry, who one by one dropped out of the chase, and a harsh, derisive cry—"CUCKK-KK-KOO!"—came floating back faintly where three diminishing dots dissolved into the profundity of blue.

Sipping procrastination like wine in the scented warmth, the drone swung faintly to and fro for hours, watching the summer pass. Indolent in body, he charged his memory with all the sleeping beauty of minutes that could never be lived again. How many who fret and fume each day away must travel all the twisting road from birth to death and never know the glory of the earth; but he knew it and welcomed each tiny manifestation as a lover welcomes each change of light and shadow on the face of his adored. What profit is it to live a thousand years and never taste the poppied honey of such a summer afternoon?

The shadows of the trees moved round with everlasting patience over the sun-dappled ground; and presently the edge of one such shadow touched the drone. He shivered, stretched out his silken wings, and quietly sailed away high in the brightness of the sunshine towards his own oakwood.

On the way, his attention was attracted by a cluster of honeysuckle twining in a hedge. He came down lightly, and hung entranced for perhaps half an hour, like an eavesdropper suddenly unable to move because he had trespassed while the very breath of summer conjured unearthly, paralyzing music from the honeysuckle-horns of elfland.

As he hung there, he saw a woodland tragedy. In a copse a hundred yards away, he noticed a wood pigeon sitting joyously on her nest. She looked very queenly in her lovely gray, with her graceful head glancing as she moved. She rose presently, and two downy squabs were visible on the platform of sticks that was their home. She stood looking lovingly at them, preparatory to flying off, perhaps to fetch food.

Suddenly, a black-and-white whirling flock of half a dozen magpies swept into the wood and flew straight at the nest. The dove flustered up to face them, but the weight of their dive swept her off the edge of the nest. Instantly she was in the air they all engaged her with beak and claw, savagely pelting her, ripping her feathers, and forcing her, wounded and bleeding, away, pursued by three of their number, while the rest turned hideously round and struck at and devoured alive the downy babies that had nestled, only a minute earlier, beneath their mother's warm breast. Not content with this, the magpies exultingly kicked and tore the loose sticks of the nest apart, and flung them to earth. Meanwhile, thrust down and overmastered by numbers, wounded and ravaged of the nestlings and the home she had so loved, the dove, lamenting, fled to seek the comfort of her mate.

The drone saw it all, omnipotent, from his leaf. He neither praised nor blamed, felt neither pity nor excitement.

An early rabbit scuttered at the hedge's foot. Instantly, with Pan-like merriment, the drone dropped almost on to the timidly lifted ear, and roared such a pibroch in it that the rabbit vanished like a thunderbolt of softest brown and white, pausing only when twenty yards away on the lip of its hole, to thump its hind feet in a tocsin of fury and warning.

And so, yearning once more for the well-filled honey vats, the drone slipped across the clover meadows, which thrummed with industry more energetically than ever in the sleepy heat of the early summer evening, and falling into place on the aerial road thronged and packed with honey-gatherers streaming with moving wings like the ripples of a two-way river, he returned to the gateway of his own city. It was crawling with workers, but he did not blame them for that, merely alighting rather lopsidedly on their tired backs and riding in that way, a sort of merry Caliban uproarious at the shrill complaints from below.

He drank deep, preened himself, remembered with joy the imperfections of the two strange cities he had visited and knew that home comforted him, then decided to take one more deep draught of that immortal day before the western sky began to fly its evening banners across the blue.

He strode out, whizzed his wings to fill his tracheae with air so that the fanners were grumbling for hours afterwards, and leapt up, ringing in wider and wider circles, turning head over heels in the air, sideslipping, zooming, diving at colossal speed. From one such dive, he straightened out suddenly and clasped at a passing leaf, swaying there so violently that the leaf was almost detached from its stalk.

Something like apprehension stirred in this little exquisite pellet of living dust which had never known anything but fun and love and warmth and happiness before. Down below him, where the first evening shadows were furtively gathering at the trees' feet, was a badger. Its bulk, bigger by many times than the whole city in which he lived, moved slowly, and the striped white head had an air of patiently seeking something. It went almost silently, scarcely moving the dead leaves, turning that colossus head from side to side, and carrying the brushy tail high enough to avoid trailing it in the twigs and dead stuff of the wood.

The drone clasped its leaf tighter as the huge thing below rubbed with a coarse and hairy side against the sapling, and set every twig violently trembling. Somewhere behind those all-seeing eyes, community memory of badgers stirred in this bee who had never seen or heard of a badger, and there was a queer uneasiness that recognized that here was a creature of the night walking by day, as weird and terrifying as if the sun shone suddenly out at midnight.

The drone shot into the air and sped like a bullet straight into the city. As he passed the sentries, the wings stiffened on their backs, and at that signal the reserves resting in the guardroom among the heavy fortifications of the gateway poured out and ran bristling about the pale, following one another in single file and staring all over the universe with fierce, challenging eyes. Instinctively, the workers crowding through the gates thinned their numbers, as though clearing a deck for action. Many heading towards the fields turned suddenly back, and massed in black regiments inside the gates. Others coming in loaded down with honey or pollen stopped in their tracks, looked back, then, seeing no instant danger, hastily shot their burdens into the nearest cells pell-mell, and spun round again lightened and fierce.

In the distant wood, the sound of the destroyer's footsteps drew quietly and patiently nearer.

CHAPTER THIRTEEN

Lord of the Wildwood

THE badger was starving. Only the insatiable craving of his belly had brought him out in daylight; his hunt all through the hours of the previous night had rewarded him only with a few insects and an unsatisfying gnaw at the roots of some trees. His daytime sleep, usually so sound, had been faint and nightmarish, disturbed by a groaning hunger. The blazing hours appeared interminable. As soon as the sun was low and shadows filled the oakwood, he stirred from his earth and lumbered along slowly and relentlessly towards a place his instinct had noted down long ago as a possible food reserve in the event of famine.

One night in late spring, his nocturnal wanderings had brought him close to the oak tree in which the bee city was located. Turning his head from side to side, and sniffing delicately, he became conscious of the faint humming, and of the fragrant sharp smell of new honey. This badger had never eaten honey; but it smelt good to eat, and an instinct from ancestors who had often torn out bees' nests or overturned beehives and regaled themselves on succulent larvae, adult bees and honeycomb, recorded indelibly in his memory the location and appearance of this place. He even stood up against the split trunk to measure the distance to the hole where the entrance to the city was, and studied with beetling brows the condition of the rotted wood. In the silent moonlight, he remained reared against the sloping column, minutely examining the substance of the dead bark, and calculating where his teeth might wedge into the cracked wood and his tremendous jaw rip lumps of it away. On that distant night, the sentries had poured out through the gates and poised above him. They did not attack needlessly, but scurried about filling their tracheae ready to take off, and flexing their stings. The badger regarded them with red-rimmed eyes each bigger than their bodies. Presently, he scuffled down again, and wandered slowly away. But he did not forget.

Something sinister in the files of tiny black defenders aroused faint dislike in him, something approaching fear. In this oakwood at night, he had never met anything that frightened him, and in his whole life had never, in fact, known fear. But caution muttered something, and for a month or two he left the bees alone. Now, however, hunger persistently reminded him of that sweet, sharp smell, and of the little sounds of mouthfuls and mouthfuls of insects moving with delicious life. So he quested through the wood without haste, far more concerned, really, with the unfamiliar bright light of evening than with the uneasy emotion that some dim memory of the bee sentries caused, and that made his coarse fur bristle now and then along his back.

He was a splendid creature, thirty inches from nose to tail-tip, the black striped "badge" on each side of his white

face boldly prominent, with the massive shoulders of a
small bear. Like most badgers, he never hunted with his
mate, though she might be seen, very often, trailing him
through the wood several hundred yards behind. They had
raised a most successful family this year, and this was one
reason why food had become so short, for over-population
spells famine with beasts as with men. The cubs were hunting on their own now and had insatiable appetites. The un-
seasonable hungers of the very young frequently brought
them out before dusk, so that when their parents ventured
above ground, the wood had been swept clean of food already.

The bee sentries smelt him coming long before he rolled
into view. The rank effluvium caused their quickening wings
to stand transfixed, their legs to bow ready for a spring, and
their stings to thrust forth needle points. One of them
hurtled into the air and circled the tree, dropping back
again on the landing stage where two others pounced at it
savagely as if for practice, without engaging.

Inside the city, as the awful smell of danger penetrated
to the furthest streets, it stilled the busy commotion of
work into a fatal calm. Regiment upon regiment of workers
moved into place behind the fortifications of the gates. The
queen and her maids, attended by two of the most polished
and formidable sentries, retired on to the newest comb and
crouched in a crevice of the most recent excavations in the
very heart of the tree. The younger nurses took charge of
all the combs of brood, faithfully warming and tending the
thousands of eggs, larvae and nymphs, and gently assisting
bees who were being born to break out of their cradles. This
released a large number of older nurses to form battalions

behind the packed troops of the workers. Newborn bees, silvery gray with baby down, quickly ate what honey they needed and formed up round the queen, shepherded by a few nurses, so as to impose their bodies between her and the peril. The last workers, coming in from the fields, ran through the endless ranks by the gates, flung their loads down anywhere, and took their places ready for battle.

The badger shuffled into view, moving in the gathering shadows, his head turning this way and that as he sought for the honey scent. A few yards from the tree he detected it quite clearly, and stopped. The sentries uttered some warning note, and immediately the massed regiments of glimmering black moved out through the gates, orderly as Zulu impis, and covered the whole of the alighting ground. Some began to march quickly round the trunk to take up position in ambush at the back. Others hurried up above the gates where they could power-dive down to the impending attack. The sentries quietly directed each column to its place by a quick jerk of head or wings or a sidling, menacing rush. While the badger was still sniffing, thirty thousand picked troops had taken up battle stations and waited with every muscle tensed for the whistle of the first sentry's leap through the glowing evening air.

The combatants regarded each other straitly. The badger felt a menace that fluffed his gray fur upright, making him seem huge and bristling. He waited there motionless in the depth of shadow, snuffling and beginning to dribble. To the bees he was a supernatural monster. It was to them as it would seem to a city of men if a creature ten thousand times the size of man, looming over the highest church tower, vast as a walking mountain, approached with intelligent and terrifying intent.

Curving like a monster crab so as to keep in the lengthening shadow, the badger rolled to the assault, like one treading through a crust of lava into Hell. The wings of the first sentry into the attack shrieked shrilly like the whistle of an officer leading troops over the top. Before the badger had lifted a foot and put it down again two thousand bees had flung themselves into the blind depths of his stinking fur and were roaring with rage because they could not fight their way deep enough through the blinding tangles of it to find a surface into which to pour the venom that seemed to be bursting from their swelling, burning bodies. Each bee felt herself expanding illimitably like a balloon of acid being pumped fuller and fuller, and with legs and wings and abdomens and heads and extruded stings they scrambled and shoved and tore and bit their way deeper and deeper, using each other's bodies as leverage, screaming so that the air all round the badger seemed horribly to vibrate on a higher and higher intolerable note.

His head, where his hair was short, was so encrusted with bees that it seemed as if he had plunged into a bubbling bog of black slime. This coating crawled bodily in the dying light like a disintegrating mask, and bees fumbled with horrible, avid little fingers at his tightly shut eyelids, and panted with starving hate to find a way through the bunched fur into the tendrils of his inner ears, and plucked and scratched and scrabbled at his iron lips, and fought one another like devils to crack off or bite through the stiff, cane-like hairs that guarded the red way up his nostrils into his brain.

The badger quickened his pace into a waddling run, and stood up against the tree, clasping it unshakably in his short forepaws, and quietly rubbing his chest against the bark. Hundreds of the shock troops bunting their bitter way through the jungle stench there were instantly broken and squashed and torn to death, and others horribly injured; these latter stuck out their stings till some of them were ruptured trying with fearful malice to touch something before they lost consciousness.

Meanwhile, the badger opened and shut his jaws quicker than light, grasping in that steely vise the edge of the hole and sending a canine tooth smashing through the waxen fortifications of the gateway, and grinding down the bodies of a picked squad of fighters there. His horny lips only uncovered the protruding teeth and drew tight like tense, coarse leather protecting the rest of his mouth, while he snorted continually down his flaring nostrils to try to blow out bees which were packing them now, killing each other eagerly so as to form a smashed pulp that would suffocate him by choking the air passages entirely.

He drew his head back steadily, and the most frightful sound the bees had ever heard rent through the oak as a great wedge of rotten wood splintered bodily away. The waxen walls were sundered, and freezing evening air poured like cold water into the ragged cavity where whole streets, with thousands of nurses and babies and eggs and pollen and honey had been suddenly fractured away and vanished, leaving the torn white half-bodies of larvae drowned in a tidal wave of pouring honey from broken and bruised cells.

All the while, regiment after regiment of bees was taking off in aerial formation and pouring themselves, like a burning oil thickly distilled from poisoned bodies, on to the badger's head, into the stretched armpits where the leathery hide was thinner, into thickets of hair beneath which some hateful instinct told them were open scratches from accidents, between the cloven cushions of his toes, into his stinking anus and hot abdomen and thighs, and ever more and more devilishly levering at the corners of his lips and nostrils and the hairy darkness within his ears. And most and fiercest at the obstinate cracks that covered his shut eyes, where bees intelligently dragged, some at the upper lids and some at the lower, while others wedged their heads into the slits until their skulls burst, and others sat shuddering with effort trying to pierce the clamped crevice with needling stings.

The badger, covered now with perhaps thirty or forty thousand bees, snuffed and struggled blindly, brushing his head with a forepaw to smash hundreds of attackers, wriggling his chest against the trunk, rubbing his cheeks on the bark, and smelling for a fresh grip on the broken city. Again his mouth cracked open and shut, grasping and breaking away a whole comb. He dropped to the ground with the comb in his mouth, heavily drowning cohorts of bees about his jaws, and went lumbering quickly away, the air round him shrilling with the noise of his attackers, and hundreds circling him in the air.

As he went he shook his head like a marionette, and uttered a low, whining growl of mortal agony. Trying to carry away the comb without biting it off short, he had admitted half a dozen bees to his mouth before he could pull together the leather curtains of his lips. His tongue swept them round and smashed them all, but one, dying, managed to sink its sting like a poisoned thorn under that scarlet curtain, and dragged itself clear, leaving bowels and poison-bag attached to the sting, before the tongue's responsive tremor flattened bee and bag together and so hosed every drop of poison into the wound. The stab of it surprised the badger just enough to loosen by the tiniest touch the muscles that bolted his eyelids down on one another, and before he could think, three stings had pierced the pupil of his right eye.

Swallowing the comb whole, and with honey running from both sides of his mouth, where drowned bees feebly and remorselessly struggled to use their weapons through the yellow flood, he lumbered into the stream with a swirling splash and began to dip his head and paw at it pitifully. Thousands of bees were drowned, some washed off and floating away down the river and turning in helpless circles, trying not to get into the air but to swim upstream again to return most directly to the attack. Infinitely more gasped out their lives under the water, where they refused to rise, and fought vainly to force their stings into the skin against which the bedraggled fur now lay closer. But the cold, choking water killed them, and if some forced their stings at last into the leathery hide, the badger cared for them no more than thorn pricks.

Only he kept scrabbling at his eye, and puffing bubbles of water thick with drowned bees from his nostrils, and intermittently plowing and plunging away downstream; and over his back and floating tail and frantic head hundreds of bees whined and whizzed and flung themselves down at any bit of him that appeared, as if they were a legion of devils.

As he drew further and further away, groaning and splash-

ing, numbers of them whirled round in a screaming curve
and shot back to the ruined city. Thousands of reserves were
gathered there, pouring over the alighting platform and
about the trunk and patrolling the air and swarming over
the torn-out piece of wood with its pitiful wreck of squashed
and shattered streets, corpses of nurses and brood floating
in pouring honey, eggs washed out of their cells and
stranded, and broken fighter bees, mostly dead, but some
still painfully retching and stirring and slowly and spasmod-
ically showing their stings.

The badger plunged through the water till he reached the
outskirts of the village. Then he struggled on to the firm
ground and lumbered round towards the hazel copse, leaving a black trail of water, like blood, in which drowned bees
showed like clots. Many attackers still flew over him, and
hundreds were whining viciously in his fur. He stopped,
rolled to kill some of them, and ran on, pausing now and
then to rub at his blinded eye. It would never see properly
again, for the three little darts, dragged this way and that
by his furious efforts to remove them or ease the burning,
had hopelessly scarred the lens.

In the tree, while regiments of furious bees rushed feverishly about in the night air, and turned ferociously at each
other, and patrolled for hundreds of yards so that every
living thing turned aside from that circle of murderous bit-
terness, work was going hastily forward. Nothing could repair the awful devastation completely, but every fiber must
be strained to put the defenses in some sort of order, save
as many of the young as might be rescued, count the frightful tally of the dead, and reorder the living so that the
sacrifice might not have been in vain.

CHAPTER FOURTEEN

Summer Night

OVER the ruined city the stench of the attacker hung like a poisoned fog, pierced by the vicious flights and whining drone of patrolling bees.

All through the summer these bees had been patient and sweet-tempered, working their long hours in the fields or in their city uncomplainingly, treating all strangers with docile friendliness so long as none attempted to invade the city itself. Now all that had changed. For the rest of the year, and perhaps into next year, a savage readiness to be first in attack would inspire them all. If a strange bee blindly pushed its way into a blossom where one of them was it would be lucky to escape with its life. If any animal or insect, no matter how large or how minute, approached within ten or fifteen feet of the oak, it would be slaughtered if possible, or hurt and driven off if too large to slay outright. Night and day sentries would be on watch to guard the dead area round the trunk, and even, sometimes, to sweep twenty or thirty yards out to seek any approaching living thing. Bees, like men, return blow with blow, hate with hate, and murder with murder.

These had, perhaps, more reason than men have for their cruel temper. If this catastrophe had happened to them a month before they would not have resented it so mercilessly, for then they would still have had the honey harvest before them. But it is the misfortune of their race that enemies seldom attack them until almost all the food that can be garnered for the year is already stored. Then they come, one after another, breaking and killing and stealing, when nothing can regain what is lost.

In the dimness of the summer night the bees began frantically to set the ruins to rights. Of some seventy thousand adults, ten thousand or more were missing, mostly drowned, while burrowing deeper and deeper under water into the badger's coat. One comb of brood had been eaten whole, with the two or three thousand eggs, larvae and nymphs within it, as well as several pounds of honey and a store of priceless pollen. Half of another comb had been torn out when that fearful rent was opened in the trunk as the badger dragged the wood away, and a third had its edge ripped off and teetered insecurely. The lower half of the second comb had broken away as the wood was pulled out, and collapsed in a frightful mess of smashed wax, drowned bees and grubs, on the ravine where the gates had been, so that a sluggish river of honey oozed out and coiled silently down the trunk to the ground—honey that had cost innumerable working hours and lives to gather droplet by droplet during thousands of flying miles up and down the fields. The gates and the heavy wax fortifications that defended them had gone, and the chill of the night poured like a river through streets where temperature and air-flow had always

been regulated to suit the hospital needs of babies being
born.

That was the first task—to cover the shivering brood,
protect the eggs and the still nymphs. Bees hurried clustering, giving the warmth of their bodies freely, for in this baby
life was treasured the slender hope of surviving into a
community future.

To and fro amidst the frightful mess and ruin went squads
of rescue workers, builders, navvies, storehouse packers. The
living were dragged and eased and lifted from under the
collapsed walls and out of the choking floods of running
honey, and were massaged, cleaned, brushed, warmed and
brought back to life so that they could immediately add their
reviving strength to the salvage operations. One bee, hauled
bodily from the crawling honey, would be seized by four or
five who would lick it clean, straighten its bent wings, rub
its feet, and press warmth into it by bodily contact. Another
would be scientifically cut from beneath a great piece of
fallen comb, brushed down and set to work.

Larvae and eggs shaken from their cells were rescued
and put back in clean, dry, empty ones on a safer comb.
Gangs of bees seized lumps of comb and levered and fought
them into new positions where they would prop up a falling
wall or dam the menacing advance of a honey river that
threatened to drown a gang of workers further down the
street. The severed edges of cells where comb had broken
away were hastily bitten together to stop more honey pouring down. The flow of honey out of the dark crevice where
the gates had been torn away was tackled next. This was a
formidable task, and several of the bees were drowned before the engineers could complete their immediate project

of casting sufficient broken wax and rubble across the lip to confine the flood into a huge lake.

Not until then did the work of carrying out the dead begin. They were picked up without ceremony, for life had no time for it, and flung over the lip to the foot of the tree. Presently the city was cleared of corpses, except for one or two still buried by the bigger heaps of rubble. The frightful disorder started to show the glimmerings of a communal plan to which each and all had been working.

Meanwhile, the queen had silently taken up her sacred rôle, impelled by a new urgency. She moved steadily and swiftly across the inner empty combs, placing eggs in patches of cells as quickly as she could move. Disaster to bee life could only be finally repaired one way. The cradles must be filled. What did she think of this blasting tragedy that had swept away thousands of her children and devastated half her domain? She thought nothing at all of the past. Her body was the flame that must light the future, and she was the guardian of the flame.

All through that summer night, and for many days and nights, the urgency of the work ousted all other tasks. A few honey-gatherers were dispatched to the withering clover fields, but almost every bee slaved at tidying the breakages, carrying outside all debris, biting up broken wax to use it again in the repair of combs and the housing of the fallen honey.

Before midday on the day after the attack every drop of this spilled stuff was licked up and replaced in sound cells. This was the first main work to be done, for if the honey were left its smell would attract robber bees in their thousands, and perhaps bigger and worse enemies as well. Moreover, each drop must be saved, or the community would die of starvation before next spring's main honey flows.

An entire new gateway with a set of guardhouses and fortifications had to be constructed, and this was erected in a marvelous way. Long splinters of oakwood had been left across the entrance where the badger had torn that great rent; and these were masoned together with all the toughest and oldest broken wax till they formed an impenetrable bastion with an entrance little bigger than a thimble. This entrance was not direct, but led to a wall of wood whose building was the greatest triumph of all. Hundreds of bees had clustered on this splinter, bending it slowly down by their weight and the combined beating of their wings, till a squad of them below could leap on it and gum it everlastingly into place with resinous propolis they had gathered, and then weigh it down with almost a handful of broken wax, bitten into minute scales and carried there and cemented into a single hard lump, filling the fissure like reinforced concrete except for the tiny entrance hole. When the entrance passage reached this blank wall it ran along its base, turned in through a split in the wood, and so reached the inside of the city. In the honeycombing of these gate defenses were guardrooms for the sentries and for reinforcement regiments. Only two or three bees could come abreast along that entrance passage with its overhead pop-holes and blind corners; invaders would jostle death at every step.

As the summer night of the badger's attack dragged its weary hours towards the dawn, stealthy creatures on silent feet and wings prospected the environs of the oak, magnetized by the fragrance of the spilled honey. Moths drifted noiselessly around, like little ghosts above the legions of the dead. Through the sweet, gentle air, their eyes gleamed enormous as they glided among the trees; and whenever one drew near, a cloud of maddened bees darted at it with a noise like a falling whiplash and sent it into the dark of the thickets. Beetles glimmered as they hastily shoved leaves aside in their progress towards the pieces of comb dropped on the ground, and the honey splashes from the badger's mouth. Thousands of bees guarded each fragment of comb and each drop of honey, fiercely fighting even the parched earth of the woodland as it tried to drink in the spilled sweetness.

They sucked it up, and drew frantically at the earth to extract the last dampness of the loss, and wherever there were larvae or eggs, bees clustered tightly and savagely over them, guarding them from voles and shrews and glittering scarabs and fighting columns of ants. Here and there a weird battle developed, for sometimes the ants refused to be turned aside, and advanced in solid regiments, at which the bees scuttered with their wings and kicked and snapped; and the soldier ants tried to fight back, seeking lodgment on the bees' bodies and attempting to sting them. Crowds of ants were killed; some bees were stung and whizzed up and down in agony during intervals between the heat of the fight; here and there solitary larvae or eggs were picked off and borne away by the raiders at the center of solid masses of formidable jaws and stings and prehensile legs. Dead bees were cut to pieces by the ants and dragged off by teams of them; so were the dying, but these the bees did not trouble to save, sacrificing them gladly, so as to occupy the raiders with something else, while the young life that mattered most was picked up and flown back to the shelter of the city streets. No wounded bee was assisted. Indeed, if it attempted to jump up to one of the clusters on the ground, it was ferociously beaten off, and perhaps its wings were torn off so that it could not return. Bees have no pity for the sick or injured; their duty is to go at once to the city graveyard and die there, and if they do not do their duty they are mortally injured so that they shall recognize that there is no hope of avoiding it. Always and in everything the community's health and fitness must come first; there is neither food nor shelter for anything less than the perfect.

So all through that long and sorrowful night, broken columns of the maimed dragged their dying bodies faithfully towards the graveyard by the river. Hundreds failed to reach it; but they had performed to the best of their failing strength the task of removing themselves as far as possible from the city, so that no infection blown from their moldering corpses should threaten those who still lived. Soon thousands of tiny winged and footed creatures of the wood formed avid crowds through which these wounded columns passed, and waited with the awful patience of wild things for the meals that were dying before their very eyes. As one bee or another dropped out and rolled over, it was quietly collected by those who waited and borne away through the leaves or the air to feed babies who needed life no less because others had to die that they might be brought the stuff of it.

A viper slithered up presently and observed the scene with cynical eyes. He picked off a few bees, but only to satisfy the undying malice of his race. Perhaps, he who would have starved himself to death if made captive rather

than accept food from man, hated these little creatures because, at times, they meet man docilely and do not turn their
venom against him except in self-defense. While the viper
was there, other hunters silently hid themselves; not even
hunger could outmatch the cold fear he brought. The bees
did not attack him nor he them. When he regarded with
hard, unsleeping eyes the disorder of their ruins, and let
his tongue flicker a little towards the place where some larvae lay, the bee warriors gave him back stare for stare. He
was not afraid of the stiff-winged cohorts, but he knew it
would be wiser to leave them alone, so he went back to
picking off a few more wounded, insolently glancing at the
others again as if to invite their comment. After some time
he went away.

Towards morning the badger circled the oak timidly at
a distance of several hundred yards. Now and then he paused
to listen for the whining approach of a bee; but he was outside the pale, and they had enough to do elsewhere. He still
rubbed his eye pitifully, though the pain had almost ceased.
He could not understand why things looked blurred to him.
He was still very hungry and sorrowful; he did not remember why. He was picking his way to a place that all the
creatures of the woodland knew well, and which they visited
in extremes of fear and sorrow.

It was a thicket where the undergrowth grew with fecund
luxuriance; and round it at broken intervals, like the last
decaying monoliths of a Stone Circle, were a few aged oaks.
The trees looked dead, yet they stood toughly, and somewhere in the shattered frames the sap still crawled at midsummer. The badger slunk forward to the middle of the
thicket, slowly forcing his way through nettles and weeds

and brambles. Safe from disturbance in that deserted place, he lay down full length, grunted and shifted once or twice, and presently slept. A little later, when the first stains of dawn silently sharpened the outlines of the trees, he shivered and stretched and got on his feet again. He scratched absently, and then turned and lumbered back towards his earth. He still saw blurred images where they had been clear before, but now he could not remember that they had ever been clear.

CHAPTER FIFTEEN

The Swarms of Death

A DAY or two after the badger's attack, a black bee glittered in the sunshine outside the oak and was instantly attacked by two sentries.

It turned to escape, but another sentry met it in mid-air and seized it by the wing before it could alter its zigzagging career. Both fell to the ground, with the first two pursuers on top of them. Almost before these had gripped the soil with their clutching feet, the intruder's wings and head were torn off, and the fight was over.

The three sentries, quivering with horrid eagerness, grasped the dismembered parts and flew with them on to the alighting platform before the city gates, on whose repairs gangs of workman bees toiled. There the broken black body was distributed in full view.

Just as gamekeepers display the dead bodies of robber vermin, just as the grinning heads of traitors were nailed on to city gates in other days, so the bees make public the remains of a dead robber—*pour encourager les autres.*

The sunny hours that were now so vitally urgent seemed to pass like minutes. Every hour meant a little better chance of survival, one more course laid in the waxwork defenses being thrown up so hastily about the broken gates of the city.

For none of its inhabitants had any illusion about the future. The wounds on the dismembered body of the black robber were like open mouths shouting to others to come and take their revenge.

At dusk that day a second black scout was caught high up on the oak trunk by a solitary sentry making the final rounds for the night. The sentry glided up from behind and bit the intruder in two at the waist before it even knew it had been struck.

That body, too, was carried down and laid outside the gates. Next morning, bees passing in and out clambered over these broken shells unemotionally; but each was careful not to kick them aside out of sight.

That day passed without incident, but again towards evening a black patrol of three fierce, shining old bees appeared. It was apparent from the first that these were picked warriors. They flew in close formation and beat off the dart of a solitary sentry with contemptuous ease, as if they had done it often before. Nor did they waste time maneuvering. Wingtip to wingtip, they dived down the air and leapt into the gateway, flinging some late workers there off their feet.

As the three poured up the narrow entry a defender dropped on the back of one of them. Its head was bitten off by one of the blacks as its feet closed on the invader's wing, but a convulsive movement in dying sent a sting deep into cringing flesh. The two survivors doubled round a corner and up a gangway into the city.

The combs were crowded and the blacks vanished into the mob. Pursuing sentries united in a shrill siren-moaning which was picked up all along the combs. Workers stopped their tasks, nurses left half-born bees unattended, every creature there lifted its head, tensed body and sting, and stared into its neighbor's face.

But the robbers had been on such expeditions before. Expertly, they shouldered into a mob of young bees. Themselves droning out the warning note, they swiftly filled their honey sacs. The young bees stared at them, but were too flustered and bewildered to act. They had never been out of the city, and though an instinct made their anger stir, they were too innocent to recognize the discomfort. They had never been angry, and had no idea what to do except make uncomfortable sounds and gestures.

The blacks, fully loaded with stolen sweets, darted down the comb towards the gates. A nurse spotted them and turned to pursue, followed by a savage old worker with one pollen basket still full. In a flash, several hundred bees had joined the hue and cry. A murder hunt was up.

The blacks doubled, darted through a pop-hole in a comb, leapt on to another, and backed down a deserted crevice. Then they made another rush for the golden gates. Only the veteran worker with the full pollen-bag held to the trail. She ran mute, leaving droning to those who had energy for it. With deadly intelligence she swerved aside suddenly direct for the gates.

The two robbers saw her turn, and abandoned doubling and hiding. The thing became a straight race for life. It was obvious that the worker would head them off, and they closed almost shoulder to shoulder and jumped at her, just as the inner defenses of the gates were reached. One wing, with which she beat off that double rush, was gripped and dragged out of her by the roots.

Spinning in agony, she never lost her vindictiveness, but managed to strike at and break off a black hind leg, and then grasp the cripple over the thorax. It staggered on without losing speed, till she flung all her weight on to the broken stump of leg. Together they rolled over and over out through the gates. The unhurt black turned and gave her a slashing coup de grâce. She fell dead; but a hundred bees poured out of the entrance and all over the wounded robber's body, tearing it to shreds and flinging them into the air.

But the other robber spun up off the oak, eluding a score of flying attackers, and whined away through the wood and out of sight.

The uproar in the city did not cease. Swiftly, as when the badger came, the fighting regiments began to mass. This time they formed their glimmering companies inside the gates. Only the sentries patrolled outside.

All work stopped except essential nursing duties and a feverish narrowing of the entrance gates. Thousands of bees disposed of their loads, tidied the plaza inside the gates, and brushed themselves into a state of polished readiness. Others snatched hasty sips of honey to add to their strength.

For about two hours they stood to arms, never doubting that the attack would come. For where one scout enters and escapes invasion follows inevitably.

The successful robber flew half a mile down the valley to a straw skep, and passed inside. It made no effort to put the honey in a cell, but swaggered up and down the streets, swinging its abdomen and staring round on the throngs

of black bees there. These black bees are the old English
strain, hardy and terrible fighters. They smelt the stolen
sweets, and first a group and then a crowd of blacks began
to surge in the leader's wake, all swinging their abdomens
and twanging their wings. Some leapt ahead and around,
others jumped on each other with mimic savagery like Ne-
groes in a tribal war-dance.

And this was indeed a war-dance with an ordained and
frightful end. Street by street was mobilized in this strange,
exciting way, and soon tens of thousands of blacks were
pouring along in a disciplined mass, fiercely sweeping into
their ranks any who tried to work or to escape.

Then the whole mob of them, still led by the robber,
began to throng towards the gates of their stronghold. This
organized, stimulated demoralization of a huge and orderly
community is a horrible thing to see.

Within five minutes of the entry of the first bee, thirty
thousand robbers, like an air fleet on its dark way to preface
a declaration of war, were flying in close formation. Here
was none of the gamboling of swarmtime, but a straight
flight boring the oppressive summer air.

They took their way, led by the robber, first to a small
beehive in a garden nearby, where a late cast swarm was
recently established. Smothering the sentries by sheer numbers, they fought their way inside. There was no battle, only
a brutal, senseless slaughter. The defenders, outnumbered by
five to one, surprised and disheartened, gave up the fight
almost as soon as it began.

Then followed a strange thing. As at a signal, the victors
stopped the avid satiation of their lust, to which they had
given full rein as they marched to and fro massacring thou-

sands of cowering and unresistant bees. Instead, they stretched out their bloody tongues and licked the shrinking banded forms; and instantly at the touch the sin passed and spread among those who had escaped being put to death, and who thus greedily accepted the alternative.

They, too, preened themselves; they began to shove out of their holes and corners, flinging off the corpses of their sisters, whose dead bodies had hidden them. They blustered and pranced and ruffled it with the invaders; then first a few and immediately all of them committed the final act of perfidy and plunged their heads into honey cells, robbing their own home.

They turned, with honey wet upon them, and invited the invaders to help themselves; they ran with horrible eagerness to and fro to show where the best combs stood. All joined the perversion. Nurses abandoned their little charges, and stood wagging approving heads and even assisting while the blacks tore half-born babies out for sport, and flung them away, or deliberately cut down honey cells so as to drown little living nymphs, unable yet to move, who watched what they did with conscious, terrified eyes, like dying novices in a waxen nunnery.

Within a few minutes the blacks were in the air again, with thousands of reinforcements from the raped hive streaming behind them, corrupted and polluted with unnamable sins against their own little sisters, flying fast as though the laughter of Hell blew behind them . . . and leaving something even worse, a smashed, leaking, violated city, all its honey stolen or wantonly spilled, stinking to high Heaven of matricide—for among her dismembered and outraged guards lay the body of the young queen.

Many bees in the frightful alliance were loaded with stolen honey. Yet they headed ferociously for the oak. They were gorged and could carry no more; but once bees begin aggression and butchery, like humans they cannot stop.

This time, however, they would meet no quisling army. While the black cloud of disaster was still approaching, circling the nearer trees, feinting to attack, the sentries of the golden city marched calmly up and down before the assembled regiments, watching the discipline with sour pride. Then the attackers came down like a dark hailstorm and the battle was joined.

Debauched with murder and robbery, and intoxicated with success, they flung themselves in legions not only at the main gates but at every crevice and cranny that might somehow lead into the city. The oak crawled with them. Too mad to care what losses they suffered, frightful numbers perished in the gates, filling that whole area with a warm, plastic mass that writhed in one huge death-agony.

Disciplined and directed by the sentries, the golden bees struck till they could hardly move for sheer fatigue of killing. But they, too, suffered decimating losses. The first drunken rush carried the gateway and swept through into the city itself. But the golden sentries, such as were left of them, knew what that rush had cost the invaders, and were grimly content.

Like a tide flowing in, the blacks and their sotted allies took the gate and the plaza within and then began steadily and mercilessly to brush every living thing forward in front of them along the combs. The golden defenders clung till they were cut to pieces, and it seemed that the pieces still fought. The first comb, where the pollen stores were, was captured and flowed with black troops, hundreds of them mortally injured. The floor below was inches deep in moving bodies. Most were dead, but many vainly trying to drag themselves elsewhere to die, quickened the mass sickeningly.

The second comb was attacked, and steadily cleared. There was brood here, and in an orgy of senseless cruelty, it was torn out by the blacks and tossed into the air. Somehow, they could not sweep the last defenders away from one corner of this comb. Perhaps their orgies were telling; all the invaders now carried full sacs of honey, and the greed which inspired them was also their ruin. They were tiring.

Into the bridgehead in the corner of the comb fresh golden troops flowed steadily, pressing and pressing against the line of fighting blacks. The invaders' contemptuous mien changed. Suddenly it was they who were fighting for their lives.

Coldly, the golden sentries threw more and more reserves on to this narrow front. It bulged; was forced back by incredible gallantry and ferocity; bulged again—and burst the black line into rags and shreds. Golden hordes began to run through the gap in a torrent, a masterful tide.

A disturbance arose in a new quarter. A reserve army of blacks had hacked and bitten their way clean through the transparent propolized barriers where the rainbow colors beat into the golden city at sunset. They poured in behind the main body of defenders, cutting them down, and tried in an insanely vicious drive to reach the golden goddess, who stood furthest from the carnage, watching the slaughtered thousands of her children with divine pity.

The small bodyguard around her tightened into a solid ring; but there was no need. An old sentry, hairless and hideous, backed by a hundred picked warriors, had been lurking in ambush, just for this, ever since the first blacks began to cut their way in. All that time, more than two interminable hours, this sentry, cruelest of the whole population, had been quivering with an insane hunger to join the battle whose proportions seemed hardly sufficient to satisfy that shaking lust. The forlorn hope of the invaders was trapped and not one bee escaped. A patrol was set to watch the broken entry, and then the rest of the defenders swept down into the main battle.

Retribution had begun. The blacks, smashed into isolated groups and companies, were being slaughtered. They had given no quarter; now their turn had come, they asked none. They died, as they had come, in utmost savagery, stabbing, piercing, maiming, laming, mutilating and killing. The circles of golden fighters crushed remorselessly in tighter and tighter round the struggling blacks, trampling the wounded down, and presently mounting the eminence of the last broken bodies before turning unslaked to tighten the hold on another doomed ring.

One comb was cleared, the next occupied, and whining columns of vengeance cut the black ranks to tatters and began again to mop up the groups one by one. That comb, too, was washed clean of the black taint; but at what fearful cost!

Then came the fight to clear the gates. The traps and passages and overhead holes built for defense were turned against the defenders themselves. But nothing could stop that rising tide of yellow savagery. The invaders never thought of retiring. Every one died with his head turned inwards towards the city. The blacks and their bloody allies went down side by side, each as pitiless as the other.

They were swept out onto the alighting place, and off its edge. The battle went on up and down the trunk, and in the grass below thousands of dying were rolled upon and crushed to death by hundreds of living locked in a last grip.

Not one invader flew away. That dark horde was wiped out as if it had never been.

The battle was over at last. Hundreds of golden bees still moved systematically searching the piles of dead to administer a pitiless final stroke to any of either side who still lived. Then they began to clear the thousands of dead out of the city, and away from the oak.

The work went on hour after hour, even when evening had fallen. A pitiful army of wounded crawled and slithered down the oak trunk and began their last weary march towards the graveyard by the river. As these unselfish columns trudged, falling and staggering, the silent army of the scavengers gathered once more on each side.

While these little creatures waited for the Reaper to send them their harvest, worms poked up blind heads from the rich soil and drew down faintly stirring bees to horrid burial; the birds stood on twigs in the last light of the setting sun and sang their hearts out, thanking God for the meal that crept below them and that had been so tragically prepared.

CHAPTER SIXTEEN

Heather Seas

FOR three days after the robbers' attack, work in the oak went desperately forward. Though the material damage was negligible this time, the frightful havoc caused by the badger had not yet been finally made good, and now staggering losses had been suffered among the adult bees, and many hundreds of nymphs and larvae and eggs had been wantonly destroyed by the black invaders.

The streets seemed sadly empty. The encounter, which had lasted perhaps two hours, had killed about fifty thousand bees, nearly half of whom had belonged to the golden city. At the height of the battle, a thousand or more were slaughtered every minute; even man must pay respect to such a rate of senseless decimation. The skep colony was wiped out; the black community would perish through lack of numbers within a month; the golden city, victorious yet fearfully reduced, faced the future with trepidation.

It was immediately decided to reduce the size of the city gates, and to complicate their defenses still further. Special gangs of workers were dispatched to the coniferous trees for a mile round, and to the plum trees in the village down the hillside. In the joints of branches, and in places where old bark had split, these seekers found what they needed—glutinous propolis, which they loaded expertly into their pollen baskets and bore home triumphantly. The red-brown, treacly substance was applied to seal up the rainbow entry, to stick twigs and chips of wood into place on the defenses, and finally to close every tiny crevice where cold air might enter during the winter.

These bees had never seen a winter. Even their goddess knew nothing but summer days and nights. But the evenings were already growing more chill, and race memory warned the bees that an invisible, icy presence was moving stealthily down from the north, against whose fatal breath they must urgently prepare.

Big teams of workers were sent out on another errand. Pollen was needed, not merely for day-to-day use in the nurseries, but as a store for use until the "palm" should meet the springtime sunshine again with its unlimited loads of bee-bread. So the bees glided in thousands over the hedges that were still starred with late dog roses, seeking the willow-herb with its generous Saxe-blue pollen, and eagerly forcing open the young blackberry blossoms. Patches of thyme and marjoram hummed with them, each bee scrupulously gathering only from its own type of flower. The outer combs of the city became jeweled with pollens red and green and yellow and white and amethyst.

A curious tranquillity followed the robbers' attack. The city, having lost so many of its older population, seemed crowded with young bees, always more good-tempered and idealist than their elders. These young bees were perfectly happy in the events that each summer day brought. And there were fewer drones. Since the badger's attack, no more eggs had been placed in drone cells, and a score or two of drone larvae had been removed from their cradles and carried out to the graveyard.

Just before that first attack, the lime trees in the village churchyard broke into green waves of sunlit bloom. Countless tiny florets swung and sailed as the breeze moved them in the sweet summer air, and gave out their faint, sharp perfume. Even when the repair gangs in the golden city were working their hardest, thousands of workers were spared to travel to and from the limes, and bring back glorious loads of pale-green honey.

There came a period when the deafening humming in those tall trees died away and ceased. There was little other honey to be found, and everyone turned to the task of preparing the city for the winter.

Then, as though the world had suddenly put on a royal cloak, the heather bloomed. Over the top of the tall hill behind the oakwood, and reaching down from there in slope after endless slope into a purple distance, danced millions upon millions of fairy bells of the color of spilled ruby wine.

Instantly, it seemed as if the golden city was to be deserted. First hundreds, then thousands of bees shot into the lambent air, meeting that bitter-sweet perfume, and sped in multitudes to the purple seas of heather, where they sank down, and, each fondly pressing open a heather bell, passed into the purple velvet interior, reaching out their tongues deliciously for the amber honey.

Imagine this vista, stretching for miles above the edge of the sea. To the bees, it would appear like uncountable little amethyst rooms, going on for ever, and with the fragrance of them coming like a lover's breath. In each, a little store of lovely nectar. Never a fear or thought besides this illimitable bounty and perfect beauty. Never a care for tomorrow or a memory of yesterday. Only the strong sun today, the honey-sweet air with the faint saltness of the sea in it, the magic loneliness where man's cruelties and follies cannot come. Life in amity, for, as well as the thousands of birds busy eating the heather seeds, and the millions of insects sunning themselves or preparing their winter store or home, and the scores of tiny animals going each intently about his busy concerns, there were black bees from the robber city, and banded Italians from the vicarage hives, and sturdy mongrels from the farm skeps; but so plentiful was that purple bounty and so mellow the autumn sunshine that wars and sorrows were forgotten, and only happiness remained.

Many of the bees ventured as far as the cliff edge, and looked down with wonder, as they swung through the great arcs that the heather sprigs crossed under their tiny weight, on the crawling expanse of blue, flowered with the white blossoms of foam. The sun made a broad golden path across it, so splendid that it seemed like the road to God.

Some of the bees discovered a mouse's nest in the heather, and hung observant for a moment watching its doings. Exquisitely plaited of heather stems into a perfect sphere the size of a cricket ball, it had no aperture; yet it contained seven little mice, naked and blind, who filled every atom of space within the nest.

The tiny mother, squirrel color above and white beneath, whisked her adventurous way through the formidable forest of the heather stems, and up the fearful branch on which the nest was hung. Neatly, with tiny forefeet, she removed and forced aside some twigs at one side of the nest, to create space for her head. She looked sharply within, apparently counting her babies to satisfy her peculiar maternal anxieties, then emerged and urged her body backwards through the aperture, most skillfully administering a teat to each blind but urgent baby head. While feeding them, she watched the bees sternly, obviously warning them against approaching so close that their drowsy hum might alarm her little ones. The bees complacently left the heather bells that were too near her, and so a little magic circle of maternal solicitude was created, from outside which the muted murmur, and the whisk of silver wings, made a tiny lullaby.

Only once was the mouse mother disturbed in her duties. A snipe came sailing down over the illimitable heather, its tail feathers humming a strident note. Urged by some obscure fear, the mouse slid outside the nest, closed the aperture at incredible speed with a couple of flicks of those forepaws like pitiful hands, and darted to an exposed place a yard away. The snipe, of course, took no notice, being far too grand a bird to trouble himself with any shrew; he went drumming on and landed, diving into cover precipitately. The mouse, which had offered her life to distract attention from her nest, turned timidly and went back to her impatient family.

The bees paid no attention to the snipe, though they watched groups of swallows which gathered in huge numbers over the heather during the afternoon. Swallows have no objection to snapping up a bee or two as they glide and sail about seeking smaller insects; on occasion, one will select a bee for sport, and pursue it through an intricate design where life and death are the prizes, the bee doubling, standing still, flying backwards and sideslipping, the swallow short-circuiting and checking and vaulting in the air, so that one of the most amazing displays of aerobatics in all Nature is gracefully exhibited in the summer sky.

These swallows were gathering ready for their migration southwards. There were many very young birds with them, for they breed on into the autumn; no one knows how such fledglings can face the journey to Africa undismayed. At present, young and old were circling, wheeling, sliding, diving and mounting over the heather, gorging on the tiny insects that played in clouds in the hot sunshine there. Sometimes the swallows glided down over some water in a shallow pond circled with purple blossom, splashed the water with their pretty breasts, and drank the spray as they passed on the wing. One would go down and sear the silver surface and pass on, followed by half a dozen others, perhaps of its own family, who shot through the rainbowed drops with bills agape, and seemed to shake their feathers proudly at the feat and to hurl off superfluous droplets.

During that honeyed afternoon the tens of thousands of observant bees noticed, infinitely high in the blue, a quivering speck. Instantly it came, the swallows vanished. All but one, too young and gay to care in time, over whom the black speck dwelt and came sliding down the miles of sky and struck with horny talons—an arrogant male sparrow hawk, which beat with long wings away over the cliffs, grasping the swallow cruelly to still its dying writhing. The old birds would have been too fast for it; and it paid no attention to the thin, twittering wail that passed with infinite sadness up to an impartial Heaven, as the mother of the little victim circled helplessly over the drop of blood which hung like a weeping ruby to a heather stem on the scene of the sudden tragedy.

There was a strange sequel. Several of the swallows, perhaps relations of the dead, swept into the air behind the sorrowing mother, and followed her closely to the pond. There, with inconceivable swiftness, they settled shoulder to shoulder along a tough heather branch that stretched over the water. This branch bent slowly down with their weight till the row of birds, all facing the same way, hung only an inch or two above the surface, in which the depth of the blue sky was intensely reflected, broken by their own shadows.

There they clung motionless, though all their kind were back again quickening the sunny air with their lovely flights over the heather distances. But these mourners stared as if hypnotized, down into the pond, as though they looked into eternity, striving to discover where the soul of their little sister had been withdrawn. All through the breathless afternoon and on until it was too dark to see them, the row of still shapes remained there brooding.

The bees, going and coming about their labors, saw without emotion everything that passed. The miles of purple glory, which would have seemed empty to any human onlooker, played out a million tragedies and comedies that afternoon, and every afternoon. Innumerable lives were suddenly cut off; others came joyously to birth. The bees saw great hates culminated, vast fears oppress, enormous labors achieved—often without any apparent purpose. Ants staggered dreadfully under colossal loads far bigger than themselves, and then hurled them down senselessly and rushed away. Tiny creatures built parts of exquisite dwellings and forgot them before they were completed. Insects killed other insects as unintelligently as man kills animals for sport or other men in wars.

During the later afternoon, the bees, who were tiring, were considerably inconvenienced by a shower of cobwebs that lasted for half an hour or more. These cobwebs were spun by very small spiders, who mounted to the tops of thousands of heather sprigs, shot out the webs from their tails with tremendous rapidity, and then leapt straight upwards into the air, without any assistance from the breeze. They floated up for several feet, some of them almost out of sight, and then gradually sailed down again, using the webs as parachutes.

Not only did flying bees constantly become entangled in the rising and falling showers of silky net, and fall roaring to the ground, whizzing their wings and kicking their feet frantically, and then have to spend priceless minutes biting and brushing and combing, and stretching out and preening; but bees engaged in the hearts of heather florets found the whole bell suddenly enveloped in a dragging mass of sticky threads inextricably crisscrossed and fastened, as a man in a small tent might be if someone flung a twisted fishing-net all over it. The bees rushed to and fro in the blossoms, shaking and vibrating them, and presently cut and shouldered their way out, only to spend much more time trying to cleanse themselves of bits of gummy gossamer.

Those who were not so unfortunate helped the victims to

get free. They crawled importantly round and round them, dragging off strands and knots of web, and even stood face to face with exhausted bees and relieved them of their honey loads so that the enmeshed ones should be unburdened in the struggle for freedom.

Meanwhile, the tiny spiders who caused all the trouble, hurried urgently about, usually ending by mounting some new heather stem and spinning a fresh parachute, and then leaping upwards into the sky again and sailing down, yet another tiny aeronaut in the floating silvery confusion.

During the late afternoon, the thousands of swallows increased to myriads. They came floating in from every quarter of the compass, and vast numbers sailed daintily out over the sea and back again, as if foretasting the joy of the coming flight southwards with the escaping sunshine. The light flickered and glimmered on their slender wings as they glided in formation and passed over and under each other in lovely curves, and twittered with excitement. Presently, the bees saw them sinking down like falling clouds, and perching on the taller heather and the shrubs and bushes for the night. And all the time, the mourners clustered still as shadows on their drooping branch over that still pond, lying like a burnished silver mirror flung down on a vast cloak of purple.

The bees took their last loads of honey home. The huge moorland, silent in the sunset, was visited only by a few straggler bees whose weariness could not stop them from making a last flight. Presently, even these were still, and soon a full moon sent a shimmering glitter-path across the faintly moving waves.

In the oak, among combs heavy with new honey, the bees murmured contentedly. The fanners were still at work, but in an hour or two, even they would be silent. Already, a teeming new life—the life of the night—was stirring in the heather seas.

CHAPTER SEVENTEEN

The Pale Horseman

ON the following day, the swallows flew southwards. The great concourse of birds wheeling
above the heather had been a serious annoyance,
and a source of some danger to the bees; yet there was discomfort in the golden city as soon as it was known that the
swallows had set off across the sunlit miles of sea. The
expanse of purple shone just as it had done the day before,
promising endless honey and pollen; neither birds nor spiders interfered today; yet there was a curious apprehension,
reflected in the sharper darting of the sentries, and the
nervous response of loaded workers.

The day was one of those of stillness and sunlight that
come only in the autumn. After its urgent springtime and
all the magnificence of the summer panoply, the earth
glowed with the glory that was sharpened because it must so
soon be put off. All day the drowsy murmuring of bees
comforted the air, and there was a sense of things ripening.
The sky over the heather shivered with innumerable thousands of bees weaving a pattern on silver wings, and the

purple bells swung madly in their fairy steeples as the honey-gatherers ran in and out.

As this day, and its unshadowed successors, wore past, a sinister affliction crept upon the bees' city. It was customary that hundreds who set out at dawn, and brought back one or two—or many—loads of honey, did not appear at evening, and were never seen again. They were the old bees, content with their little lives, who felt the stiffness of death come upon them suddenly, perhaps, as they lay in the embrace of a heather bell, and so stretched out well satisfied and ready for sleep, and fell unnoticed amidst that purple glory. Or perhaps the whisper of the scythe came to them on the wing, and their splendid eyes grew sightless and the worn-out bodies glided silently to earth for the last time.

But now a new happening sent a chill through the city. Some of the young bees, only a few days old, began to move with lethargy very strange to them. They went about half asleep. They forgot to eat, or plunged feverishly into a honey cell only to cease feeding and wander away as if thinking of something else. Instead of vibrating and moving their wings in the joy of living, they crawled leaden-footed as though they had no wings at all. They took to standing still for long periods, and when workers friendlily bunted them out of the way, they fell over, lay prostrate, and presently got up stiffly, making no protest and apparently not remembering what had been done to them.

When they were engaged in nursing duties, they showed neither pride nor pleasure. They went about their work as if drugged, dreamily completing tasks by instinct. They made hardly any sound, which was indeed a portent; for normally the nurseries were occupied by a continuous din day and night.

Some of those who were afflicted with this strange tiredness graded on to field work. Instead of flying ecstatically into the splendor of the heather hills, they struggled along through the air as if weighted down by nightmares. They took far longer than they should have done to gather a load of nectar, and then stood dreaming on some heather stem, perhaps for half an hour, before falling from it and somehow regaining activity in the drowsy air, and beating their heavy way home again.

The affliction spread. The terrifying thing was that it spread among the young bees only. The old workers were as eager and excited and joyous as before—until they regarded the silent groups of handsome youngsters, standing as if turned to stone, or dragging themselves to and fro from the honey fields as though they in their generation were conscious of a secret sorrow hidden from all else.

The older workers were amused at first, but swiftly passed to indignation. At first, it was comfortable to boast that youth was not like that in former days, to deplore pitiful weaklings who could do less work in their prime than worn-out bees with only an hour or two more to live. But this mood passed. Fear and anger replaced it. The first sufferers were hustled outside, and the sentries crossed forbidding antennae clashing behind them to forbid any reentry now or ever.

The soft young bees stood melancholy and silent on the alighting platform outside the gates. There were half a dozen of them at first. They made no effort to return, nor did they protest or move. They were not in the way of the streams of workers, and there seemed nothing specifically wrong with them; so long as they did not turn and try to enter the city, the sentries left them there, having much to do to check every bee that flew in at such a busy time.

The fugitives did not protest. They did not stir. They stood wherever they had been left, neither communicating with each other nor taking any notice of the throngs that raced past them. Sometimes, an incoming bee would alight on their backs, half playfully. They took no notice, only clung more tightly to the tree. Clung desperately. On that first evening after they were expelled, a returning forager, overloaded with pollen, dropped awkwardly on to one of them, and leapt off towards the gates. The shove of that kick knocked the silent bee over. It rolled on helplessly, and fell heavily on to the ground at the foot of the tree.

The rest crouched closer. It was as though a shiver passed through them. They made no effort to enter the city as the chill autumn night closed down. In the morning several had gone; two remained crouching as they had been the night before. They were alive, breathing heavily and hard. During the morning one rolled over the edge. The solitary survivor tried to climb up the trunk. Very slowly, it dragged itself a few inches up the rough way, then fell backwards and down to the earth.

Swiftly the mysterious sickness spread among the young bees. In a few days scores of them were affected. They seemed to find it difficult to breathe. Air was cut off from parts of their bodies, which distended and stiffened. Their wings set at horrid angles and could not be moved. Only with the utmost difficulty could they crawl about. They became unable to eat or do anything to help themselves.

Instinct forced their slow feet to drag them outside the city. They crawled in hundreds down the trunk on to the ground and began the dreadful walking procession towards the graveyard by the river. But they could not get far.

One morning, some of them, feeling death almost at hand, attempted to climb grass stems near the oak. With prodigious labor, they reacted to the final bee desire—to mount as near to the sky as possible—and reached each the top of her stalk of grass or weed. There they clung, slowly stiffening, staring with hopeless eyes on the woodland beauty about them.

Soon scores of them, and then hundreds, clung paralyzed to the stems all round the foot of the oak. They remained quite motionless for many hours, some of them surviving a night. While the top of each stalk held its rigid bee, others waited urgently below till the one at the top should fall to the ground; then they stirred their stiff members in a macabre race in slow motion each for a vacated stem.

Those who fell moved very little. They bent and stretched their legs, and tried to move immobile wings, and died.

Inside the city the inexorable law of survival ordered that each victim, on the first onset of the attack, should go voluntarily outside or be hustled there. Many hundreds were so suddenly stricken that they could not move, but crouched, impotently beseeching others to carry them outside where the death in their bodies might not harm the community they loved.

Sorely troubled, remote in her divinity alike from sympathy and assistance, the goddess tried to stimulate her birth of new baby bees beyond the instinctive rule for this time of the declining year. She knew that death could be foiled only by birth. Moving quietly from comb to comb, she saw the numbers of her eldest children dwindle swiftly from work among the heather, while the newborn were decimated by hundreds through this shadowy plague.

None of them knew how it had begun, or what caused it. None realized that this hateful legacy was left them by one of the robber blacks, who had picked up the mites which block bees' breathing passages when indulging in his first theft. This dark intruder had spied out the weakness of the swarm-skep, contemptuously loading the stolen honey and swallowing simultaneously the invisible seeds of death. This same robber, supported by two as wretched as itself, had penetrated to the honey vats of the golden city and left in them some of the mites with which its body was loaded. It had taken away enough to cause its own death while winging at the head of the invading army towards the doomed skep; it had left enough to infect and exterminate the city in the oak, to the last bee, unless some stronger fate intervened. So pestilence always follows war.

Each mite, a crude organism less than one-hundredth part of an inch in length, invisible when swimming in honey even to the tremendously powerful eyes of a bee, sought a living host. Established in a bee's breathing passages, it bred with nightmare enormity, swiftly closing those passages, paralyzing muscles, and opening the road to invading death. Mites spread from bee to bee, and not there only, but shed themselves on the blossoms of the heather, and so were picked up by bees from other colonies. Like a foul, invisible mist, the plague spread in ever-widening circles far and far from the oak and the village and the surrounding hills.

For a long while there seemed no remedy. Work in the

heather dwindled at uncanny speed, not from the golden city alone but from everywhere around. While the moors hung heavy with nectar under the autumn sunshine, fewer and slower bees came there each day, and thousands rolled out of the velvet florets down to dusty death, their tasks half done.

Like an invading spirit, the Pale Horseman galloped across the landscape rich with that fatal purple bloom. In his wake, thousands of tiny figures clung rigid and silent, beading the grass tops as with a dreadful sweat. The old alone were not permitted to die—they were condemned to stare helpless and forced in every hour of the day and night to listen to the shadowy hooves beating faster and faster on the naked, quivering heart of youth.

CHAPTER EIGHTEEN

Children of Chalk

WHEN the terror was at its height, the autumn rain came teeming.

The clouds began to gather during the night, and steadily rolled and piled overhead all through the following day and night, until dawn. They seemed to fill the depth of the sky; and still more came, flowing beneath the others until they rested on the hilltops and seemed as if they must stop up the valleys soon as well. Colored a flushing purple and completely excluding the sun, they seemed like a gigantic, bruised reflection of the heather masses below.

Over the sea, there was an oily calm more portentous than wildest waves. No foam showed, yet the water boiled along in molten haste, olive and shuddering. The gulls uttered apprehensive outcries, and swooped greedily and hastily to stuff themselves before beating away inland on long, pointed wings, leaving a silence filled with a slavering growling from the caves into which the hungry tide was flowing.

On every tree inland, and every hedge and bush, the

leaves dropped as if ashamed of some crude outburst whose coming they could not prevent. Not a bird stirred or sang. The air was heavy and hot, and clouds of flies flickered round every upright thing. As the flushed dawn crept about the landscape, the heat steadily increased, and not even then did the birds sing.

The world suddenly darkened, as if night were returning. The first huge drop of warm rain splashed softly—stopped— and then began in earnest, as a vast shiver of lightning leapt a hundred miles between two clouds.

The bees in the oak tree watched it fling a veil of flashing, lacy patterning across the sky, darting to and fro, seeking the path of least resistance; and when it struck, a firmament of blazing white stars burst round the purple wound it tore in the recipient cloud, and flung thickets of streaks whirling. Instantly followed a darkness blacker than any night, in which the rain could be heard drumming through the leaves and gathering already into trickling runlets across the ground.

Alternately flaring into shadowless white and plunging into lightless black, the earth reeled under the impact of the rain. A whole order of little creatures—insects and tiny animals—was exterminated as swiftly and thoroughly as mankind in the Flood, and the ruts and ditches and rivers bore a scum of their small, sodden bodies. Leaves and twigs were broken from trees, large stones on the hillside unearthed and washed down, perhaps from the sunlight of a thousand years into some crevice or ravine of everlasting darkness.

Legion by legion, the heather bells were beaten off on to the earth. Already the florets were past their freshest beauty,

and this assault was more than they could resist. The birds
and beasts of the heather crowded trembling under gorse
bushes or in holes in the ground until the spreading and
welling of the water forced them out. Then, staggering and
hurrying and crying out unceasingly in small, frightened
voices that were borne away in the giant laughter of the
storm, they struggled to find fresh shelter, many being
beaten down and dying of exhaustion and cold.

The thunder bellowed and rolled away westwards presently, following the dawn; but the rain increased in volume
and thrashing vigor, borne by a chill wind that pushed the
hot air before it like a great cushion. All that day it rained,
and though the strength of it moderated during the night
to a fast, drenching drizzle, the next dawn showed a hopeless world of flood and mud and disaster. With the strength-
ening of the light the rain eased and ceased; the whole
world clucked, dripped, gobbled and sobbed.

And then, silently, the sun blazed out between bars of
slaty cloud, forced them wide apart, sucked up a veil of
pearly mist, and smote the drenched land with blinding
light and steaming warmth. The mist cleared, the sun grew
hotter, evaporating moisture drops from every leaf and grass-
blade, and changing the world anew into a dry, comforting,
lovely place of lambent gold and velvet-black shadow, all
newly washed and glorious.

The bees came out, first in little groups, then pouring in
multitudes, sporting on the wing and landing on every
dancing leaf, and feeling the healing warmth on their backs.
Some instinct told them with certainty that the dread
disease was going as suddenly as it had come; and this was
their time and ceremony of purification. The great rain had

washed the heather and all the world clean of the mites
that carried the infection; some trick of suddenly changing
temperature enabled the bees in the city to cast off the
weight of the plague. Some of the badly infected died; others
healed; but the young brood emerged healthy and strong,
and no more sickened.

Once more there came a time of counting the losses.
The city that had numbered more than a hundred thousand
bees at the height of summer was reduced now to a little
over twenty thousand. The new streets of fresh, white wax
stood deserted. Life had shrunk to the center combs; these
were flanked by splendid combs of clover and heather honey,
far more than the colony would require for its winter sustenance; and on these, wax-builders worked incessantly, sealing over each cell with a lid of wax. Before this was done,
the heat of the city and the work of the fanners had evaporated all excess water from the honey; now it would keep
in perfect condition for years if need be.

In the persisting warmth and sunshine of the autumn, the
queen steadily continued her task of laying hundreds of eggs
each day. The nurses tended them as busily as ever, knowing the urgent need to increase the number of the population before the cold weather stopped all further births.
This unremitting, loving labor entailed the feeding to each
individual larva of about thirteen thousand meals each day,
one each minute or so of the twenty-four hours; but it was
never neglected or skimped.

Steadily, the numbers increased again; not nearly so
quickly as in the pregnant springtime, but still with splendid comfort, as the autumn brought day after golden day.

From her seclusion, the queen-goddess looked out across

her golden city with sorrowful eyes. Some instinct warned her that, though the plague that had decimated her children was checked, an impalpable shadow still touched the oak tree. Everything seemed well. Numbers were steadily increasing, autumn blackberry bloom was adding to the already ample honey stores, no enemy approached. Perhaps she felt in her own body the seeds of disaster impending.

The bee nurses had the first news of it. Passing to and fro in joyous haste among the nursery combs, they were arrested by a sudden murmur from one of their number. She was feverishly licking a young larva whose cell was all ready for sealing up—in fact, the masons stood by, waiting to begin the job that, normally, should have been an occasion for ceremonial rejoicing.

The larva, which should have been comfortably curved in its golden cradle, was stiffly stretching its body straight out. It was dying.

Death among the brood reduces all bees to terror. They will face out, with a courage that seems to approach the callous, a disease that strikes only grown bees. But brood death pierces the communal heart, chilling the zest for labor and the passionate selflessness of defense, and replacing it with lethargy and hopelessness. For, if the brood dies, what object is there in living—since community life itself can be only a thing of weeks.

The little half-born bee, with its dawning sensitivity, slipped swiftly back into oblivion, darkness and cold. Its mourning nurse pitifully worked to lift it out of the cradle. Already, the small body was stiff. It seemed somehow attached to the wax of the cell. As she struggled to release it, and then, failing all else, began to bite out and cut away the walls of the cell, the body changed slowly in color and—horrible metamorphosis—in consistency. It ceased to be pearly white and shapely; the sharper outlines set rigidly into a sort of crude mass; and the whole assumed the texture of solid chalk.

While this was happening, a score of other nurses announced similar discoveries elsewhere.

This was not natural death. Occasionally, a larva would be somehow accidentally injured in the rushing business of the city and would die; or, even more rarely, one would be somehow improperly fed. But this swift calcination of the dead body boded something far more terrible.

During the ensuing hours two or three score of larvae died, stretching themselves out straight in death and changing swiftly to impalpable chalky lumps. Some were cut out of their cradles and carried outside. But soon the nurses lost heart. Fear paralyzed them. The thick white shapes were left in the cells where they died, in dread negation of that first of all laws of bee life; that a passionate cleanliness shall rule above every other habit.

A band of the senior nurses went in deputation to their goddess. The maids who attended her opened their magic circle to let the cortege in, and observed it with stilled wings and troubled, sorrowing eyes.

There was some communication between the deputation and their sibyl. They bowed and murmured, and presently backed away with wildly waving antennae. The circle closed about the queen, and she began again her everlasting duties. But there was a new atmosphere in the city—the timid quickening of hope. Nervously, the workers and the nurses and the masons closing the honey vats, recommenced their various labors.

The group of senior nurses passed slowly and methodically along the combs, selecting others of their kind, here a few and there a few. Some who pushed forward were briefly rejected. Some who hung back were sternly fetched out of corners or from behind crowds. They accepted fatalistically this strange call, and fell into place behind the leaders among a crowd now numbering two or three hundred strong.

Presently, they all moved together towards the city gates, and passed through on to the platform outside. There they assembled in a gesticulating crowd, humming with suppressed excitement that bore a note of fear. All other traffic through the gates was diverted for them by the sentries; and this was done in sinister fashion, as though those who passed out were under the shadow of death, and beyond all earthly formalities. Inside, among the nursery combs, that chilling wail arose from one new point after another, as more dying larvae were discovered, and stiffened, and turned to chalk.

All together as one, the hundreds of bees rose suddenly from the platform into the air. Like a tiny swarm they set off in a close-winged cloud deeper into the oakwood. The undergrowth grew thicker and more matted and of a darker green, the trees more gnarled and closer. Suddenly the bees whirled round in a great circle, flying at a tremendous pace; below the center of that aerial whirl was a smaller circle, clearly marked by a broken ring of ageless and almost leafless oaken trunks. From above, it was clearly visible that the

woodland teemed with insect and animal life of all sorts;
but inside the circle of oaks nothing stirred. Going round
and round at vicious speed, the bees narrowed their circle
and drew closer to the earth like the coiling of some great
black spring. Tighter and tighter they drew it, till they
poured down together inside the ring of oaks, on to a dull
blue patch which seemed to magnetize the only shafts of
sunlight in that dark place. This blue patch was caused by
a straggling root of devil's-bit scabious, with its balls of
purplish bloom, each consisting of hundreds of tiny florets.

On these blooms, the bees clustered and moved, putting
aside the stamens and furtively gathering the pale, as-
tringent nectar. As they swiftly filled their honey sacs, they
jerked from flower to flower with stiff wings and tensing
stings, falling over each other, leaping suddenly aside when
nothing touched them, humming erratically and crowding
together. Yet there was nothing to be afraid of—only the
ruined old trees, the lascivious richness of the weeds, and
the silent shaft of golden sunlight staring like a great eye
at the patch of flowers. The heat grew intense.

The bees who first filled their honey sacs stood about
impatiently, stirring their wings and hopping from bloom
to bloom, watching the others. Those still working collected
nectar faster than ever.

Suddenly, as a cloud of flies will rise, the bees shot up
together, circling fast, uncoiling the spring now into wider
and wider circles. Having reached the height at which they
had approached, they went on uncoiling higher and higher,
as if to wash away in the sparkling sunlight some aura that
clung to their bodies, the scent of the purple bloom. Then,

like a handful of black pebbles rolling downhill, they raced off in a direct line towards the oak tree.

Something passed for a moment over the whole surface of the circle behind them—something like the ghost of a great sigh.

CHAPTER NINETEEN

"For the City"

THAT chosen cohort of bees which had gathered the scabious honey fled back to the city as though the Devil were after them.

The sentries swept everything aside to let them in, and they darted in a black mob directly towards the comb where the queen was at work. The whole place thrilled at their entry. Even the keening for the dead babies stopped instantly.

They began to unload their honey, as fast as they could move, into a group of cells near the queen. The honey glowed in the darkness of the place as if with some internal flame of its own. Its odor was pungent and exciting. Before even the first cell was filled, the queen's maids came to it, like virgin martyrs, and timidly, yet with unflinching resolution, took the sharp stuff upon their tongues.

Hurrying back, they crouched submissively, offering the honey to their lady.

For a perceptible second, she hesitated. Then the fumes of it seemed to thrill her mind and drive doubts fleeing away. She who usually sipped so delicately fell upon these offerings with a horrid avidity. The little maids rushed to and fro, but could hardly feed her fast enough. She turned from one to another with the urgency of a drug fiend.

Not until she was gorged and somnolent did the maids cease—not till then would she allow them to cease. Even then, as she sprawled across the combs, she reached out her tongue with drunken imperiousness, and more of the honey had to be brought.

Long ago the seekers had flown out again to fetch more, and had already returned with a second load.

At last the queen crouched inert, only her great eyes smoldering in doped wakefulness, seeing, perhaps, a procession of fantastic dreams. Her maids lay in a circle about her, watching her fearfully. After perhaps an hour she rose. The attendants instantly tried to feed her again.

But this time she turned from the scabious honey with shivering disgust. They drew back, appalled. She moved across the comb, passed right through the center of the city to the other extreme edge of the nursing combs, and there began to lay her eggs as before.

On her way, she had to pass many of the white chalky figures of her mysteriously dead children. She gave no sign of noticing them. But it was significant that where she passed, the nurses suddenly began with new vigor cutting the little corpses out and flying with them into the open air, to get rid of them there. Also, the wailing stopped.

In the course of the next few days, two or three hundred more larvae died and turned to chalk. They were silently removed from the city. The disease had never been epidemic. Only one here and there of the larvae was affected, inheriting some fatal tendency not communicated to the rest.

But now these occurrences stopped. The queen had somehow cured herself by that gargantuan banquet of the bitter honey. She herself did not know how or why. She had followed an instinct that outraged all her lovely and fastidious royalty, and now the eggs she laid produced normal, healthy, pearly larvae as before.

From dawn till dusk, in the mellow beauty of the autumn days, the bees ranged wide, joyously accepting the glory of the earth. Passing on their journeys to gather the last honey from fragile blackberry blossoms, Canterbury bells, ivy, and the poppies flaunting where corn was still uncut, they saw also the fruits which they had fertilized. The orchard was green and rosy with apples which the farm men were picking, feeding thousands of them into a stone cider press like a great well-top, in which a patient horse rotated a stone wheel to crush out the last slow oozings of golden juice. The May trees were scarlet with haws where those billowing masses of blossom had been that had so attracted the swarm. The hazels, whose shy little flowers had been so ardently penetrated in sunny hours in February and March, were laden now, and village lads and maids idled along the hedges, nutting and flirting in Arcadian preparation for their own fruition.

The drowsy hours went by, and the stolen days of late sunshine passed, while the earth stood entranced at its own beauty. In the evenings, the tired bees glided home across great fields of glittering stubble, under a clear evening sky against which the stark boughs of the trees stood out etched in black. Clouds of gnats inhabited the air over the stream,

their little chorus adding the touch of lovely melancholy
that is the true plenitude of happiness. In the dusk, as the
last straggler bees hastened home, the bats wheeled silently,
and had to be avoided; if one could catch a bee, it would
swiftly shear off the wings before eating the body, hiding
its head with its wings as a hawk does, as though flesh-eating
were an indecency. The world was alive with the noise of
crickets, and the whir of evening insects, and the brave,
sweet whistle of a late-hunting robin among the leaves at
the hedge's foot.

Many of the bees busied themselves through these autumn
days gathering propolis. Though the oak stood stiff as a
granite monument, yet some instinct told them that the
winter gales would set it vibrating like an organ-pipe; and
so that these vibrations should affect as little as possible the
honeycombs on which the cluster of bees would hang, they
fastened the combs at all available points securely with
this gummy resin. The Romans, when they found their bees
doing so, called the substance they used "Propolis"—"For
the City." Each year, many bees' lives are spent gathering
it; but lives "for the city" are always willingly available.
The work of softening and gathering the stuff is heavy and
tedious; sometimes it is used to exclude or even trap the
Death's Head moth; many ounces of it may be brought in
during the autumn, and each ounce may cost hundreds of
lives.

Every crack and crevice was filled with it, to exclude
winter draughts. Every pine, horse chestnut and plum tree
for miles was scoured up and down the trunk and branches
for the precious gum. Roads, roofs and other places where
bitumen might have been used, were scrutinized by the bees,

who dropped on each patch of shiny resin and eagerly transferred the stuff to their pollen baskets. People and traffic on
the roads; birds and reptiles and hungry little creatures on
the roofs and in the trees, rolled at them like juggernauts or
directed wickedly timed attacks. Some bees were trodden
on or rolled over, no one knowing; others were snapped up
and eaten; more, having with wonderful cunning and
strength avoided these attacks, died simply of overwork. But
what matter; the city grew daily more secure and more
guarded, more clean and garnished and ready for winter.
Though still no winter threatened in the placid days and
calm, murmurous nights.

Then came the wasps.

Bees do not fear wasps. Wasps do not invade, as other
bees invade, in fanatical armies maddened by rhythmical
and mystic war-dances, and ready rather to die fighting than
perhaps to expire later of hunger. No; the wasps come in
threes and fours together, being such rogues and traitors
that none will agree to organize with others a joint attack,
for fear of losing the sweetest of the thefts; but, like gang-
sters, a few join in a bond of villainy, each secretly hoping
that the rest will be killed so that the spoils need not be
shared.

A wasp is much stronger individually than a bee, quicker,
with twice as powerful jaws, and a sting that can be used
again and again without endangering its owner.

When the first wasp was seen, hurriedly hovering outside
the oak, shimmering up and down and making feints to seek
a way into the gates of the city, the sentries regarded it with
angry cynicism. Its tricks and subterfuges in the air were
made to try to lure them from their posts at the gates. Then

the wasp, with its longer and more powerful wings, would lead them a dance in the air, finally plunging down and into the city before they could land to prevent it. They had never seen a wasp; but they knew all this perfectly well, and crouched shoulder to shoulder, and made insulting passes with their antennae, almost as if cocking a snook.

The wasp regarded them malevolently. It pretended suddenly to sideslip, to have hurt one of its wings and to fly lopsidedly. It staggered in the air as though it must land on the oak or crash to the ground, somehow awkwardly flipped on to the trunk near the gates, and stood shuddering there as if mortally stricken. Again it was attempting to draw the sentries from their solid phalanx in the gateway.

Their wings stirred on their backs, and their jaws worked with rage, but they could not be moved. The wasp leapt suddenly in behind an entering bee and tried to rush through the gates. Two sentries met it like bullets, and it swerved lightly round and was in the air again, watching with intense care for an opportunity to make a new break.

Another wasp flickered up from somewhere. The two made no effort at alliance. They hated each other as much as they hated the bees. Whenever one tried to slip through the gates, the other raced down, too, horridly afraid lest it should miss a successful theft.

In one of these rushes, the sentries darted out just a fraction earlier than usual and managed to grab the end of a long silver wing. In the terrific melee that ensued before the wasp could free its now ragged wing, the other robber flew straight into the entrance and was instantly among the combs inside.

It darted about, dipping its head for a sip of honey, racing on, taking another gulp, shouldering off a furious nurse bee, knocking a fierce old worker flying, and jeering as it passed. The commotion it caused, however, was too great to allow it to carry out its purpose of filling its food sac. To gain a moment's respite it darted to one of the deserted outer combs and clung there, but before it could rest a mob of bees came roaring. It evaded them neatly, and began to zigzag and battle towards the gates.

It had, however, counted without the tortuous and elaborate fortifications. As it raced down a corridor there, a bee jumped expertly from above on to its back and bit it almost in two at the waist. Its impetus was sufficient to carry it outside, thrashing fiercely with its sting; there, it rolled off the ledge and on to the ground.

The other wasp instantly dropped fiercely on top of it. These creatures are cannibals if they can do no better. The attacker dispatched its comrade with a single slash of punishing jaws and immediately began to break open its body to suck out the undigested honey it had stolen at the price of its life. Having completed that, it fell ravenously on the contents of the abdomen. Presently the empty shell was rudely kicked over and deserted. The cannibal then darted into the air and began anew its patrol in front of the city gates.

No sooner had it done so than one of the bee sentries, first looking to see that its comrades were numerous enough to keep guard safely, leapt off the edge and floated down on to the ruined body of the dead wasp. Grasping it, the bee flew into the air carrying that great burden, and staggered with wildly beating wings on to the platform again. There it

laid out the wasp body as a grim warning to all who might
come.

The flying wasp was not impressed. It made an abortive
effort to use the body as cover from which to stage a rush
at the gates, but that failed. Then it pinged away into the
wood—only to return two or three minutes later, hoping to
find the vigilance relaxed. It was not relaxed but redoubled.
The bee sentries faced it sardonically.

For hours the wasp spent its furious energies trying to
break into the honey store. When it tired it went away and
caught and ate a wood fly; but only to give it new strength
to waste flickering and feinting outside the gates of the bee
city. Wasps seem to be devoid of sense in such matters.

All that day, and most of next day, it kept its post un-
scathed. The bees were content to defend; they did not
try to attack. Other wasps came. One or two penetrated the
city. Some even got away with loads of honey. They were
more or less damaged; one succeeded in killing a couple
of bees which it jumped on from behind as they were filling
a cell.

The invasion never became serious. The bees dealt with
it as a nuisance which they knew they could control. Presently some vagary of wasp nature took all the attackers
elsewhere.

The community in the oak was now comfortably numerous again. It was in splendid fettle, every bee shining gloss-
ily as if clad in silk.

Suddenly the nights grew very cold. Work had to stop
much earlier, and the adult bees clustered together during
the dark hours in rehearsal for the hibernation sleep that
now drew close upon them, and of which, being summer-

born, they knew nothing. Even the sentries were forced to join the cluster as the sun touched the western horizon.

It was in the few minutes of twilight after the sun had set and before night fell that a new intruder stole into the city. It was a tiny moth, about the size of a housefly; a little creature of grayish-brown, perhaps the most nimble-footed thing in all creation.

The wax-moth darted in on her powdered feet, and flipped up into an outer comb. The city was thrumming softly with the noise of the bees in the cluster, but they had not seen her. Running in and out of the deserted cells, she sought a satisfactory place to deposit her eggs.

All through that night the tireless, fleet little moth ran from cell to cell. She would not deposit her eggs in adjacent cells, guided by the need of her offspring which would require each a goodly area of wax to eat and destroy. She made no whisper of a sound, but passed like a tiny, furry ghost about the unpeopled outskirts of the city.

In the dawn, an early sentry moving to take its place at the gates saw the vestige of a quiver out of the corner of its all-seeing eyes. The moth had vanished into a cell and crouched trembling, but the movement as it drew its round-ended wings timidly over its body, was just too late. The bee pounced. So very swift was the moth that it was out of the cell and starting across the comb even before the bee, wing-aided, could reach it. There followed a single, savage snap, a whirling flutter of soft wings, and a shuddering collapse.

The bee gathered the little corpse up, flew down the comb and out into the cold air of early morning, and tossed the light and fluttering body free to float down into a leafy pall. There are few mornings, so merciless in Nature, when murder is not one of the first things astir.

The bee darted inside again, and back to the scene of the encounter. It ranged fiercely over the combs for several minutes, seeking more moths. Another sentry came up, half-seizing its comrade in its rage, and being impatiently flung off. They both searched vigorously. There were no more moths.

Once more the mystery of instinct came into play. One of them had never seen a wax-moth. The other had en-countered one for a few moments only. But both knew quite well that they must hunt for eggs. They went systematically along the empty combs, looking for the eggs that were not as large as grains of dust.

Here and there an egg was found sticking to some incon-spicuous crevice in a cell. It was ruthlessly torn out, carried outside and flung away. Other bees joined the hunt. For an hour or more they thoroughly covered those combs, and looked even far beyond them. They examined the interior of the tree, and the floor, and particularly the wax defenses of the gateway.

Two eggs were missed.

CHAPTER TWENTY

Death Dance

STILL that blazing autumn went on in mellow sunshine and stillness as though it would never end. The bees in the city reveled in every sunny hour. The world that had been so perilous for them had grown peaceful. Already, indeed, the somnolence of hibernation was creeping unseen about them. There was not now the rapturous rush into the air as soon as the sun touched the oak trunk. It was so comfortable and warm among the combs, so fresh and chill in the silent autumn morning outside. Work stopped, too, before the sun touched the horizon. There was not much nectar to fetch, though the days could be delightfully idled away jumping from blackberry blossom to blackberry blossom along an endless hedge, and daintily sipping the tiniest breath of sweetness from each, and then drowsing there for a while before exploring further. There were no more flower buds promising intensity of action. The trees and the grass and the flowers that started it all seemed to be resting as if their work was done.

Only in the full sunlight was it as warm, now, as in among the laden honeycombs; there was a great sense of

comfort in returning there. Little was being done in the
city; there was no more honey to load into cells or to seal
over with wax; no fresh wax was being made; the queen
had almost ceased to lay, and only a dozen or two dozen
bees were born each day, so that nursing duties were practically suspended. Fanning had stopped except for half an
hour at midday; building had ceased; those who wished
could exert themselves in adding a fresh layer of propolis
here and there, but such work was done for love, since already the whole of the city had been luxuriously secured
for the winter by bees, now dead, who had never seen and
would never know a winter.

The population moved lazily about the center combs,
admiring the faultless masonry of them, rejoicing with an
unceasing murmur at the ample food supplies of more than
one hundred pounds of sealed honey and a store of multi-
colored pollen, and delighting in carrying outside almost
imaginary granules of dust from the fervently cleaned and
polished ways.

All the time the two moth eggs were hatching in the
warmth that pervaded the whole city; and presently, secretly, silently, the little white worms which emerged began
to devour the wax of the cells in which they lay. With fearful and uncanny speed they tunneled through scores of cell
walls towards the center of the comb, where some pollen was
stored. As they worked they grew larger; for they ate the
waxen walls, and soon were eating pollen, and presently
bored into the bottom of a cell where a bee larva lay.

Up to this point they had taken different routes, but here
they joined forces, biting side by side through the cradle

wall and into the soft, unresisting body of the larva, which
stiffened out and died almost at the first touch.

Behind them these two creatures had left a gauzy webbed
tunnel which showed their trail through the pierced walls.
On the journey they had grown from almost invisible things
like fragments of cotton nearly to the size of the wingless
body of a bee.

Their own horrible greed for meat was their destruction.
They might have lived on wax at the edge of the comb, and
spun their silken cocoons, and slept, and presently emerged
as moths to reproduce their kind in multitudes. In a short
time, just when the bees were somnolent in their winter
sleep, the moth invasion might perhaps have grown to fatal
proportions, ruining all the combs, cutting and rotting them
from the oaken roof, and sending them crashing down in
a ruin of broken wax, spilled honey and miles and miles of
weblike, dirtied gauze.

But now, as each worm ferociously shoved the other so
as to guzzle faster mouthfuls of flesh, a nurse bee suddenly
stared at them from above. With incredible swiftness they
hid their bodies in the broken wall of the cell, presenting
only their heads to attack; and these heads were helmeted
in a sort of scale armor. Vainly, but terribly, the nurse bee
bit at them; then, screaming a warning that fetched thousands of bees racing to the spot, she turned round and struck
again and again at those helmeted heads with her sting.
That sting would have penetrated corduroy cloth; but it
glanced harmlessly off the armored heads of the worms.

But that should not save them! With a score of others
helping her, the nurse bee frenziedly bit and tore away the
cell walls, hurling behind her the broken, gnawed body of

her tiny dead charge. The worms turned each along his tunnel in a flash to try to escape. But there was no escape. Bees swarmed everywhere, ripping open walls, diving into cells ahead, projecting their stings, reaching down with slashing jaws.

It was all over in a moment. Both worms were bitten to pieces. The hunt went on for an hour. Every millimeter of the webbed paths was torn out. Every cell was searched. The last traces were removed and shudderingly flung outside.

But several times that day bees rushed furiously about on a false alarm that other worms had been seen.

All that day, and through the ensuing chill night, there was uneasiness and activity about the city, and a curious murmur that grew very slowly yet appreciably in volume and took on an ever more urgent and warning tone. In the dawn of a cloudless day, and on until ten or eleven o'clock, this sound increased.

Only the queen and her maids took no part in it. They had withdrawn to the edge of a comb in curious isolation. The queen remained there all that day, tragically watching everything that took place, unable in her divinity even to avert her head; for among the powers of godliness in creatures self-pity is unknown.

The time had come for the slaughter of her sons.

At first the drones hummed louder than anyone, reacting as always to communal excitement, stumbling to and fro with enormous importance, and appreciating every movement in the whole throng with their bold and magnificent eyes. At other times, if they did this when a community activity was in progress, they were good-naturedly bunted out of the way or head over heels by the workers; but now all that had changed. Wherever a drone passed he was treated with a sort of piteous love and respect, which made the good-natured blunderers timid and uneasy.

As the warmth of the day increased little groups of worker bees began to move together about the combs. At first this seemed no more than chance. They went up and down the golden streets as if searching for something which they could not find, perhaps which they did not even know. There was no rhythm or direction in it at first; sometimes one group would come face to face with another, and each would turn hastily round as if ashamed of being noticed, and go quietly and quickly away. But as the minutes passed and passed, it became obvious that there was somehow a connection, at first vague and then marked, between these movements and the pulsation of the general humming.

It was at this juncture that the drones ceased adding their voices to the harmony. They fell suddenly silent and crouched impotently where they stood. They clung fiercely with their feet, turning sharply to look at other drones, and from them to the singing concourse of the workers. These were gathering into regiments, steadily moving in an emerging measure, and singing a muted hymn whose form was becoming unmistakably that of a fugue.

Yet it did not lament at death as humans do. The splendid recurrence of that harmony held the undying beat of the great pulse at the heart of things. Immortality proclaimed itself. Beyond the alternation of waking and sleeping was a glory everlasting, a beauty flawlessly above the momentary touch of pain and decay. A triumph fundamental and eventual, in which the dancing grace notes of a single summer and the lullaby called Death formed no more than a momentary incidental air in a majestic and everlasting symphony, no note of which would ever be lost.

The drones, as they crouched in the lengthening shadows, began to understand eternity and desire it with a cracking of the heart. Their glowing eyes pierced the darkness and saw amaranthine hills. The pacing choirs of workers steadily speeded the pulsation of their triumphant psalm till the heady fumes of it swept and rolled—and then dissolved in misty banners rising to disclose Heaven's bluebell fields.

All the thousands of choristers, moving through the figures of a mighty consonance, added, troop by troop, the vital harmonies of a single all-conquering unity. The oak became sonorous like an organ-pipe. The bee dancers, gathering momentum like the waves of an incoming tide, took direction and coherence. Very gently at first they swept, singing, a little way towards the city gates, then ebbed back a little, and then forward, while the pitch and rhythm of the dirge gathered irresistible emotional force.

The drones did not wait for the tide to reach them.

Almost all together, like things enchanted, they rose up from crouching and stared at the golden light where the sun struck in at the gateway. There was something symbolic in their movements—the turning from the darkness of their terrestrial home towards the distant glory. Never heeding the singing throng behind them, they walked quietly and with dignity towards the gates.

Instantly scores of bees detached themselves from the rising tide, ran forward to the drones, lovingly touched and caressed them, smoothed their wings, glossed the brown velvet of their coats, and removed fanciful specks of dust from about them. Others, sinking down in their path, proffered drops of the most delicious honeys that the storehouses contained.

It had an air of worshiping admiration, all this, as well as tenderness and pathos. They were saying good-by. The drones, who had always seemed such clumsy, simple creatures, carelessly tolerated, were loaded suddenly with an almost hysterical affection, and garlanded with memories. Hitherto, such an outburst would have hurled them into paroxysms of oafish gesture. But something emanating from the rising tide of victorious sound and rhythm that came rolling behind them sobered them now to an aloof gentleness that was almost royal. They accepted the offerings of honey, and the caresses, the hosannas and the prostrations, graciously, as royalty blesses with the hand the suitor must kiss; nor would they delay, but kindly put aside those who were importunate, and walked on steadily towards the sunlight as if, escorted and heralded by that united throng, they walked alone.

The sentries stood ranked at the gates, and as the first drones passed between them, their antennae rose as though they were presenting arms.

Still with that air of creatures under a spell the drones took off from the alighting platform into the hot sunshine. They circled once, to face their old home and to hover, staring at it with their great eyes—and then turned swiftly away and beat out on strong wings into the unknown.

Of those first dozens who took flight none ever returned. They sped on and on across the fields, some for half a mile, some for a mile or two or four. When exhaustion, or perhaps some creeping shadow of fear or regret, tired their powerful wings, they glided down, one on to a dandelion's sunny face, another on to a blackberry blossom or into a lethal bower of dark ivy. They could not drink the nectar there—Nature had made their tongues too short for them to keep themselves. But they clung in honeyed dreams of the immensity of some unshadowed Heaven; and there, as the chill of evening struck them, so their bodies died.

Destiny had been very strange and cruel to them. They had been born; they had lived without apparently fulfilling any purpose; now, in self-abnegation, they must give up again into the Hands that sent it the tiny spark of living fire they had cherished, never knowing why. Poor fragments of unfulfilled desire, perhaps the splendid harmony of their farewell somehow promised them, in some happier day, a better part in the immeasurable pattern of everlasting life.

Back in the city the rising tide of the death dance swept irresistibly up to some few drones, irresolute and infirm of purpose, for whom the compulsion of the music had not been enough. They clung desperately to corners of the combs, tried to escape, even flung themselves in terror among the locked masses of the workers. As well try to hide from God. They were surrounded, with marked gentleness and care, offered choice foods, stroked and petted; soothed, or it may be hypnotized, by the volume of sound and the lovingly urgent gestures, they, too, presently found themselves outside the city gates.

The last drone was escorted outside, and behind him poured out a rejoicing multitude of workers, filling the gates, filling the platform, and finally, with amatory compulsion, edging him over the abyss and into the balmy air. He circled fearfully several times, at tremendous speed, and

then essayed to return, trying to land, as he had done so
often unrebuked, on the backs of the workers on the platform.

Without changing the throbbing regularity of their
hummed melody, and with a compassion more merciless
than any rage, they deftly beat him off. He spun out and
back again, uncomprehending. But he was not allowed to
land, and finally, in pitiful bewilderment, settled on the
other side of the oak trunk, and paused there for a long
while.

The multitude of the workers began to ebb, as they had
flowed out, like a tide receding now, back through the gates
and into the city. The jubilation of their song lessened, and
its volume ebbed, too. An hour after the last drone had
been expelled the sound in the city was reduced—significantly reduced below anything it had ever been since summer came.

When the sun was setting barbarically among clouds of
gorgeous colors a few of the drones tried to reenter the
gates, among them that one who had been last to go. But
the sentries drew up in rigid line across the entrance, and
these drones, who had been free of any bee city anywhere,
realized that death stood grinning in the portal of their own
home. The sentries had no sentiment. There was no need
for these intruders in the cold winter months when no
queen could possibly be born or need a mate. When spring
came again others could be raised. These had outlived their
usefulness.

Only one or two, frantic for the warmth and comfort of
the city, flung themselves senselessly on their doom. Unable
to fight, they had to accept dully the bitter wounds, the

shameful hustling, the final contemptuous jolt into the abyss in which, because of their hurts, they could no longer fly.

As the sun sank, and the cold autumn twilight gathered, all those splendid males, once so gay and careless, lay scattered, motionless and dead.

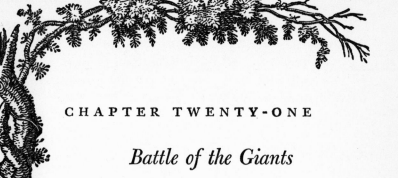

CHAPTER TWENTY-ONE

Battle of the Giants

THE first frosts of the autumn glittered on the dead leaves that carpeted the woodland.

Especially in patches of shadow, behind the trunks and in uneven places on the ground, the bees observed with wonder the millions of different starlets, crystals, and all the varied shapes of the shining grains. They saw, too, the sudden flushing of the leaves on trees and hedges, the royal prodigality of colors, and the steady drifting down of these leaves to the ground, to expose new beauties of interlaced and intricate patterning of branches and twigs against the pale blue sky.

In the lazy pleasure-flights through the warm midday air, the bees watched other creatures preparing for the winter. The bats, their insect foods vanished, betook themselves to holes in trees and hung up there for their winter sleep. Hedgehogs wrapped themselves deep inside balls of leaves and mud and fell into profound torpor. The dormice, who give the impression of being a little late with everything they do, hurried frantically to complete the nests in which they presently curled up contentedly for a seven months'

rest, fortified by the presence of a few beechnuts in case
of somnolent appetite.

Drinking bees were incommoded and annoyed by numbers of frogs hopping and trekking towards ponds and
river backwaters, where they installed themselves in the
mud with the very greatest solemnity and earnestness. They
appeared to sample the quality of the mud severely. Dozens
would congregate in one patch of it, apparently of a particularly viscid quality, and sink themselves there for the
winter in the closest physical companionship, their eyes almost popping out with pleasure as they slowly sank. Others
would stand critically watching the performance, and then,
with ineffable disdain, turn slowly and hop away to a more
elegantly muddy site elsewhere.

Toads were seen furtively digging themselves in under
the roots of trees, slowly, as if they had the year before them.
Newts crawled like tiny dragons past the drinking bees,
and sought for themselves cold, moist stones under which
to sleep out the winter. Snails were observed closing, with
infinite labor, the exit of their shells with painfully produced
membranous veils, and seeking winter quarters beneath tree
trunks or stones, while slugs slowly burrowed deep into the
earth and leaves of the woodland. Spiders, with whom the
bees observed a sort of armed neutrality, for the spider
usually releases any bee caught in its web, spun themselves
warm silken blankets, and, securely enwrapped, and protected by a leaf or projection of bark over them, settled
down to lethargy.

Centipedes crawled into sleeping quarters beneath fallen
tree trunks. Queen wasps, bloated and heavy with gestation,
crawled slowly among the fallen leaves, looking for a wind-

less, dry cranny in which to preserve their race until the summer came again. The bees could easily have destroyed these torpid queens, whose existence threatened their own community life. But bees seem incapable of malice.

Perhaps these manifest preparations for sleep exercised an effect on the bees. Instead of flying out every day, they were content, now, with less and less frequent journeys into the open air. Somnolence pervaded the city. The noise of industry had died to a faint, contented murmur, most comforting and sedative. There was no longer active movement about the golden streets; those bees who left the clustered center combs walked lethargically; and when they passed through the gates, would stand sleepily for a long time in the sunshine, jerking forward a few paces, stopping, and then filling their tracheae and taking wing with drowsy determination, economizing wing-beats to the limit.

There came a morning, at last, when the powerful autumn sunshine was clouded and hidden. The world was cold, the sky gray, the colors of the frost-painted leaves dulled. No bee emerged that day.

But during the afternoon a new and strange invader made a silent reconnaissance of the outer walls of the city. Quivering along on noiseless, tiny feet, a mouse passed between the grass stems at the base of the oak and stared up with intelligent, shining eyes. It remained motionless at the root of the tree for such a long time that it seemed to be carved there, with one foot raised; but its nose wrinkled faintly as it smelt the air to try to detect the sharpness of danger.

Then, swiftly and without a sound, it flickered up the oak trunk and stood in the gateway of the bees' city.

Again it froze into immobility. Its russet ears pricked to

the faint and distant murmur of the humming. Had that note changed it would have flung itself down to earth. Its whiskers vibrated nervously with appetite, for the smell of the loaded honeycombs was attractive and exciting.

Yet robbery was not the only motive that incited this little creature to contemplate so desperate an act as entry to this guarded city. Like the bees, it wished to hibernate, though not as completely as the snakes and frogs and hedgehogs. But it needed a warm and waterproof retreat where it might lie snug while the raving winds and killing frosts did their work. It had been lazy, wasting all the summer and autumn days wantoning with its mate, never gathering nuts for winter food or painstakingly building a weatherproof nest. Now, the weather was too cold to start nest-building out of doors and most of the nuts were gone. Overtaken by destiny, as other spendthrift lovers are, the mouse, at last, had to face its liabilities. Shelter and food must be found—at others' expense. Industry was lacking; crime was the only alternative.

Like a flash of red light, the mouse darted into the city gateway. He nibbled expertly at the heavy wax defenses, constantly pausing to listen. Presently, he had opened a tiny passage—and squeezed through on to the floor beneath the hanging honeycombs. Looking sharply round, he saw the outer combs of succulent wax, with patches of pollen and delicious honey. They were unguarded. From the center of the nest came the faint, unsuspicious humming of the bee cluster.

Hunger or arrogance caused the mouse to stride sharply along the floor beneath the center combs, every nerve atwitch ready to flee. He saw the tens of thousands of somnolent bees tightly clustered overhead, looking dreamily down on him. As he watched, they shrank a little away from him, towards the tops of the combs. They were afraid.

As with man, so with wild things—to be feared arouses hateful instincts. The mouse strutted a few paces. The bees withdrew further. The mouse sat up hungrily, with tiny forepaws on the bottom of the comb, and nibbled out a taste of honey. The murmuring above took a sinister note, but still the bees shrank back.

For this is the strange truth. Bees, which will attack headlong when a man, an ox or an elephant threatens their city, are as much afraid of mice as any Victorian lady. They, too, tuck their skirts—or, at least, their wings—about them, and jump to the highest place they can reach, and shudder and complain. Hundreds of bee colonies every winter are starved and annihilated because they dare not attack a mouse which enters their citadel. The story does not invariably end that way, but almost always it does. Something in the mouse odor is incomprehensibly terrifying to them. They will sometimes desert a honey-laden home altogether, when a mouse enters, and swarm out to die in the cold. Or they will abandon a comb which a mouse has soiled, and creep away to die on empty combs elsewhere. Sometimes—very rarely—they strike back.

The mouse examined every corner of the lower part of the city. He decided to place his nest there, his food stores nearby when he felt energetic enough to venture out and gather anything alternative to honeycomb. With sharp teeth he made a few slashes to mark the lines of his plans. Then, with a skip that made the bees crouch, he spun round and went out.

Half an hour later, he returned, followed by a young female as pert and perfect as himself. Mice are always slender when they enter bee colonies; occasionally, they grow so fat that they cannot emerge through the crevice that let them in, and so are trapped for wasted weeks in the springtime. While the greedy, charming little female squeaked gluttonously through a mouthful of honey, her mate, trying to reach a patch of fragrant pollen, darted a few inches up the center comb.

The move was fatal. Had the two invaders contented themselves until the colder weather with what they could reach from the floor, the bees would have shrunk timidly further away every day, sinking deeper and deeper into hibernation's trance, yet constantly disturbed, nervously overeating, and so tainting themselves with dysentery and fever. The mice would have eaten and soiled comb after comb; and, before springtime came again, the colony's story would have ended in silence, stillness and decay, while a family of fatted mice triumphed among the ruins.

But, by chance, that sudden rush happened to direct itself straight at the queen's majesty. With a vengeful roar, a thousand bees dropped on to the mouse, hundreds instinctively plunging in their stings before they realized that they were touching this horrible odorous thing, and shrank away.

The mouse fell, writhing in awful terror, as hundreds more poisoned darts pricked him everywhere. He wriggled convulsively an inch or two towards the entrance, looking like a pincushion of white poison-bags. He might have dragged through the entrance into the open air, but his mate, with a sideways spring like a rocket, spurned him with kicking hind feet so that he rolled over on top of a mass of fallen bees, and there received a final attack. A few tiny kicks, and presently the adventure that had begun so bravely was ended, while the sleek little russet female was bounding for her life through haunted glades that seemed to echo in her prick ears the thundering roar of angry bees.

In the city, the whole community was astir, despite the raw chill of the darkening afternoon. Hundreds went to the gates; but it was hopeless to try to repair the damage there until a hot day came when propolis might be gathered; for wax could not be made in the autumn cold. Hundreds of others rushed up and down the combs in anger and dismay. But thousand upon thousand marched fiercely round the body of the victim mouse. There it lay, on the floor near the inside of the entrance gates, on its side, the pure white belly showing vividly in the penetrating light, the handsome russet back glowing.

There it lay for two days. Then a vagrant sun came pouring down in strength, in one of those ineffable late autumn days; and the bees hurried by thousands out of the gates and on the wing, as if this were the height of summer with the clover gay in bloom.

Away they went in squadrons and cohorts, seeking propolis. A gang of navvies with a steamroller mending a road down the valley stopped their work and hopped and leaped about, shouting profanity about "a swarm of bloody bees." The foreman's sardonic advice was silenced as he himself was also convinced. The "swarm" settled intently on new patches of bitumen, and, fascinatedly watched by the men, filled their sacs with tarry glue. For this was an occasion where trees yielded too slowly; a desperate occasion for a remedy no less desperate.

Innumerable loads of propolis came back to the city all through the day. Over the mouse's body, a perfect glazed mausoleum began to take shape, transparent as the tomb of Lenin, exquisite as the Taj Mahal.

The Giant had been killed indeed—at the cost of many hundreds of precious lives. But this titanic body could not be carried outside; not the labors of the whole community for months would serve to cut it to bits and remove it; and there were not working months ahead, but only days at most. So—the body was completely sealed in propolis, red like ruby glass; for only so could its decay be prevented, and a stench that would carry death with it for them all, be bottled up. But for that, the invader who could not triumph living would have struck a mortal blow from the grave.

The little body lay there all through that winter, and the next summer, and for many years. Whenever the propolis cracked or wore thin, it was perfectly repaired. Embalmed, still with a hundred little white poison-bags stuck in its side and head, but otherwise looking as perfect as if asleep, the mouse may rest there . . . for ever.

CHAPTER TWENTY-TWO

Out of the Past

SOME instinct of coming storm, perhaps, had stirred the mouse to seek shelter at such fatal risk. A few nights later, its mate was drowned in one of the worst autumn gales on record.

The sunshine that had seemed everlasting was washed away as if for ever. Almost as fast as the merciless rain, the last leaves came teeming down from trees and hedges. The wind rushed about like a devouring monster roaring for prey. The sky lowered and took on a steady, cold gray color which persisted day after day and week after week, the weather steadily growing more wintry and desolate.

During the afternoon before the great storm broke, though the sun was still shining hotly through wild cloud, the bees in the oak began swiftly to collect in a tight group on the center combs of the city. Hundred after hundred and thousand after thousand leapt on to the faintly stirring mass of bodies, crouched down there in as little space as possible, wings folded, feet steadily gripping, and more hundreds and more thousands added themselves in successive coatings to the growing, living ball.

The cluster was formed on the empty parts of the combs just below the extensive winter stores of honey; all the outer combs were completely deserted, for the last baby bee of the year had been born and had safely emerged, and the nurseries were empty. The head of each bee was beneath the abdomen of the bee next above her, so that all were cozily protected and kept warm except those outermost on the mass.

These were the hardiest of the young workers. Later, as they grew chilled and so more wakeful, they passed into the center of the cluster, where the warmth and silence soothed them to a dreaming half-sleep. Then, when the ones who replaced them became chill in their turn, they also burrowed inwards; and the process was repeated again and again so that each took a turn outside, eventually became cold and wakeful, and moved inward very slowly to a deeper hibernation.

Only those at the top of the cluster could reach the line on the comb where the sealed honey began. They first of all passed down from tongue to tongue sufficient honey to feed the pioneers on the outside, who were braving the cold; then all the rest of the bees were fed, and finally those fed who were against the honey. Perhaps for days, in the cold weather, there would be no activity, but just torpor; then, as the vagrant warmth of the winter sun struck the oak, and enlivened the air, the bees at the bottom of the cluster crawled up over their comrades' backs and took their place above them along the next line of full cells; when these were empty, other bees came up from below; and so the whole cluster very gradually climbed the combs.

Towards the center of the cluster, the queen, still with

attendant maids who washed and fed and combed her whenever the warmth of the air was sufficient, crouched as somnolent as the rest. Her labors, like theirs, had ended for a few months, while the sun turned his beaming face away, the earth wore gray and sable, its wedding garment rotted, and it waited for spring to come again, singing to the wooing.

As the bees clustered, the humming that had occupied the oak unceasingly for many months insensibly subdued, and presently fell to a strange silence. It marked the end of an epoch, that silence which would remain until the glowing ardor of the earth's lovemaking recommenced.

The clustered tens of thousands were not still. With faint, rhythmic, ordered movements of their bodies, they created and conserved precious heat. They did not sleep. Dimly, they were conscious of each other, of the silent orderliness of the colony, and especially of the presence of the queen. They would have known had any invader entered the city or any serious disturbance taken place outside. They would have stirred and many would have gone to investigate, while others forced their drugged and reluctant minds and bodies into full wakefulness that might well have been fatal to them all; for such unnatural waking would have meant gorging with food, and then perhaps dysentery and community death.

But the woodland grew very silent and peaceful. The oak tree and all its companions lay entranced like figures in Sleeping Beauty's Palace, waiting for the sun's kiss. The bees, tightly clinging, faintly moving in the gentle rhythm that breathing sleepers use, could see and feel no longer directly through their senses but dimly and sweetly through their instincts only.

These instincts were inheritances from the whole vista of the past. Man forgets such instincts in the commotion and worry of his little life, though the tiger and the ape as well as the fawn and the dove peep out from him at times without his knowing. The bees, in the glory and activity of summer, use methodical orderliness guided by community reason. But in the winter, when all is still and silent, the body rests but the race memory awakes and ranges in the lost sunshine of eight thousand million years.

Faintly stirring in their cluster within the golden city in the oak, the bees sluggishly felt again some of the emotions of the First Things—the intertidal shellfish and flower-headed zoophytes of that weird age of naked, plantless land and sweeping, fishless seas. As slowly, perhaps, in the dim half-death of hibernation as it happened in that incomprehensible predestined march of millions of summers and winters towards today, the bees presently conceived a faded picture of the fishes that were also their ancestors, rushing through the waters of a much later world. It was a place of barren rock, without plants or soil in which plants might grow.

The communal memory of the bees, sluggishly moving like their faintly moving bodies in the cluster, becomes suddenly more defined at a memory of the first bees, millions of years before the first human or animal footprint came on the changing primitive world. Those first bees are seen flying over colossal forests whose feet stand in slime. Those bees, living in pairs or little families, not yet in communities, evade the great spiders and centipedes, watch dragonflies with two-foot wings, and nest in undergrowth by the edge of the limitless sea.

Another gigantic leap through time, and the bees remember the first clustering, in the age of the hundred-foot land monsters. Slavering with giant hungers, these masters of that forgotten world of reed forests and fern prairies turned anxiously upon the monstrous vegetation, upon the insects and the fishes, and upon each other. The giant lizards, searching out the little nests of the family bees, ate nest and young and honey together. The bees grew cunning, and hid their nests in holes in trees and rocks, instead of hanging them among grass and leaves. But other creatures came, tearing at the holes as the badger still does.

So, at last, most of the bees became communal. Some went out to search for food, while others mounted guard at home. Shrieking and croaking through that eternal summer, the winged things pursued the bees, and the animals tore at their nests, while the big bees of the dawn of life fought back in terrifying clouds, elaborating internal poisons from the hates their destroyers bred in them, and forming the dart that, under happier circumstances, might have been some sort of ornamental tail.

Constantly attacked, but bravely persisting in their tradition of never striking until themselves assaulted, the bees clung tenaciously to existence while the earth heated and cooled and warmed again. Dimly, the bees in the cluster in the oak remembered how their ancestors evolved a form of rule under the wisest mothers, who bred the finest children while other mothers became nurses only, others fighters, others wax-masons. And then, perhaps, in some vast, unrecorded battle going on for centuries against animals or cold, the males were all but exterminated, and those remaining had to be treasured for breeding alone. And how, in a million years or two, they forgot how to bite or sting or work, and became drones; while, of the mothers, the best alone was reserved for the prodigious task of motherhood for them all. So the mechanically perfect community evolved, selfless, loveless, and undying.

They remembered, and stirred uneasily in their twilight dreaming, the first creatures that tried to walk erect and turn their faces painfully to the sun. Through changing ages, they watched these two-legs with an apprehension and an unwilling regard. And then, at last, a mere forty thousand years ago or so, the apes and the submen and all the animals and the bees saw other creatures walking erect, hunters with spears and stones, before whom everything else that lived felt an awe because they were devils, and acknowledged an unwilling dominion because they were gods.

The cluster in the oak felt fear and hope flowing through them all. From the first, these men could dig out honeycomb from the rocks or break open the trees to get it. Almost from the first they commanded fire. No animal knew fire or could face fire—the bees shivered as at the threatening smell of smoke. Men took the honeycomb, using their arts of fire, and the bees felt mastery. Bees died for lack of the honey that men ate. But men soon helped bees, building roofs over the bees' nests, driving off bears and drowning robber insects. Men gathered up bee swarms, when they fainted in the sun or shivered paralyzed in the rain, and carried them into places where bee-cities could safely be established. The devil in man hurt bees; the god in man helped them. Quite early in the history of this human tribe that came so new to earth after the bees had lived there millions of years, a shadowy, uncertain alliance was begun between insects and people. Sometimes, one killed the other, deliberately or unwillingly; sometimes they helped each other. The bees found, even then, that it was wise to swarm on Medicine Days, as, later, they preferred to swarm on Sundays; on those days the devil in man was held slightly in leash, the god struggling for emergence.

Man, too, was beginning to scratch the earth's surface, and plant seeds, and from the seeds grew flowers with nectar. The priests stole honey and mixed it with blood or wine; but the priests protected the bees' communities with edict and fetish, and set hairy men to guard the waxen cities from animal invaders.

Beside the tower-like temples that sprang up along the Nile seven thousand years before Christ was born, white-robed priests chanted as they slowly marched past clay bee-hives. The architects of the great pyramids refreshed themselves with asses' milk and honey, and the race-memory of the bees in the oak remembered myriads of men and women toiling past with blocks of stone, and falling, and dying, while still the bearded architect toyed with his bowl.

The embalmers used honey, too, in mummifying the corpses of the great, and left some of it in food jars in the vaulted burial chambers, where it was found thousands of years later. The Persians carried it with them in great horns when they went journeying and warring through their mountains. Sargon packed rare seeds in it, when he sent them as gifts to the princes he intended to destroy. Isaiah made a sardonic joke about it, when he said that there was more honey after foreign invasion—presumably because the invaders changed arable land into uncultivated pastures rich with flowers.

The bees in the oak, rhythmically moving and slowly remembering, saw Isaiah clearly for a moment, a bearded prince in fine raiment speaking unpleasantly to a dark-faced king, but shrinking from his wife who ruled the clay hives and the honeypots and him with a rod of iron.

They remembered Minos of Cnossos, son of Zeus, father of Ariadne, and felt their wings shiver with anger and apprehension as they remembered him, for he not merely carried hives of bees for their honey aboard his new warships, but discharged these hives of rotted logs down upon the decks and wharves of his opponents, which they feared even more than his bull-helmed spearmen. At Cnossos, too, the bees saw man's first attempt to invade their element, the air, and watched Daedalus leap through the sky and crash to death in the blue sea with that first glider; and shivered as they knew from aeons of experience that death never turned man aside from his ambitions, and that within a few hundred, or thousand, years, man's wings would be grown.

In Egypt, the bee was used for hundreds of years as the symbol of perfect government, and Mykerinos, nearly four thousand years before Christ, took it as his symbol and named all bees sacred. The bees in the oak remembered him with gratitude.

And they remembered Virgil and Horace arguing about the value of the scazon meter as they lay drowsily beside the beehives on that farm in the Sabine Hills; and Cicero and Pliny and Aristotle, all of them bee-masters; and fierce St. John and fiercer Mohamet; and gentle Gautama Buddha, and that bald-headed, solid seaman, Odysseus, and Richard Coeur de Lion cutting up honeycomb with his sword; and those three kings who rode to Bethlehem with honey at their saddle-bows; and many another, famous or unknown, poet-beekeeper or king or warrior honey-taster; and many a woman, white or red or yellow, black or brown, like that one Solomon held up to us for ever, with dove's eyes and a tongue sweeter than honey, for whom such men wrote their hearts out, or changed kingdoms, or slew their thousands and their tens of thousands.

Passing the honey from tongue to tongue as the cluster tightened in the colder and colder weather, the bees in the oak remembered. Always, they remembered summers, million after million of vast, sunlit summers, which their race had fertilized and populated, back to the dreaming edge of time.

CHAPTER TWENTY-THREE

Nadir

THE bells of the village church were ringing in Christmas rejoicing across the snow. The oak-wood stood in the tranced silence that only snow can bring, hushing the footsteps of the woodland things that stirred abroad, and confining more of them sleepily in winter nests and burrows.

The morning was quite windless, and the sun shone hot out of a pale sky, sparkling the snow, encrimsoning the holly berries, and flashing on the cold turbulence of the stream.

Some of the bees on the outer edge of the cluster were irresistibly attracted by the sunny glitter, which flung a hard white light into the city gates. There was warmth with it, too, from the strong sunshine reflecting from the snow. The bees whisked their wings hopefully, and made little movements of their bodies which presently resulted in detaching a dozen or two of them from their locked positions.

They shook themselves free, stretched, glanced about eagerly, and then dropped towards the gates. Round the gateway was a considerable litter of dead bodies of bees and fragments of wax and rubbish. There had been a gray and icy week or two just previously, and no chance had occurred to remove this stuff.

The active bees fell upon it with avidity, carrying or rolling the bigger pieces outside, and fanning out small grains of wax or dust by using their wings, or sending it rolling through the gateway by an expert kick or two. Many of the bees whose age and tiredness is far advanced in autumn die during the winter months, and these were flung outside without any of that exaggerated sentimentality that humans use towards vacated flesh.

The tidying took half an hour or so. One or two more bees joined the clearing gang, but all the rest hid their heads tightly from the seducing light. Those who were working on the floor were indignant at this. They made an eager humming, strutted out of the gates and in again, jumped invitingly up the combs and back to the entrance, and shivered their wings. The bees in the cluster hid their heads more tightly than ever.

The more adventurous abandoned them to their lethargy. They strode outside, debating with their antennae, marching about vaingloriously, feeling the welcome sunshine soak through and supple their bodies. Then, one after another, they darted into the air, circled the tree, and set out for a proper flight high across the snowy landscape.

A quick movement passed right through the cluster, like a communal shiver. It was really an endeavor to cling tighter. Except the queen, all the bees in the cluster, at intervals throughout the winter, sped out of the city for cleansing flights; but they avoided days when the treacherous snow was lying. The cleansing flights were taken in answer to the unbreakable law that no bee may soil the city; but they were very brief, and it was wiser to take them on warm, dull days. Winter sunshine was dangerous. It lured too far.

Those who had left the city while the Christmas bells were ringing ventured beyond the limits of their strength. The blazing white light and the clear sunny air tempted them on and on, just for the joy of using the wings that had been dormant for nearly all their lives. Then, when they tried to return, the cold ate into them as they flew, and dragged them down. Only two or three crawled exhausted back through the gates, and stood there trembling, gathering enough strength for the jump up on to the combs and back to the cluster. There, they were at once admitted to its center, and felt life tingling back.

They had seen strange sights.

Rabbits and birds were scuttering in the snow, frantically trying to find food to save themselves from starvation. The birds, with fluffed feathers, looked twice their summer size. In one field was a flock of thousands of hen finches, with not a single cockbird among them. Several of them took wing to try to pursue the bees, so violent was their hunger; but in this they only wasted the strength they so bitterly needed. Why this feminine alliance? No one knows why it occurs, or where the cockbirds go in winter when such female congregations form. The others return in spring, and each pairs again with his old mate, after the females have spent a whole day twittering ceaselessly together in some final ceremony of remembrance—or maybe some convent vow of secrecy about the segregated doings of the winter months. Or is it perhaps the males who form a club and all go off to France? The bees observe all Nature's changes, but do not speculate.

They suffer sometimes from this incuriosity—though it must repay them ten thousand times in lack of apprehensions.

They would have known, a day or two after Christmas, had they been able to reason, that the steady tap-tapping on the oak trunk, just against the gate of their city, was caused by something dangerous to them. It was a curious, imperative sound: TAP . . . TAP-TAP-TAP . . . TAP-TAP . . ."

Again and again, it was repeated in a sort of tune, bitter and hard and urgent.

The bees had not seen the invader approach, for he had observed their habits for a day or two, with the terrible patience of wild things before they attempt an attack. Hour after hour, this green woodpecker had sat motionless in a nearby tree, estimating and checking when the bees emerged. Today was icy cold, with a hard wind blowing. Today they would not come out in numbers sufficient to make them dangerous; but they should be fetched out one by one, and for a fatal purpose.

The woodpecker examined the base of the oak tree first, and spiraled up it to a place several feet above the city gateway, before dropping down and taking his position on the alighting space outside it. He was a prudent bird who had brought up several families and survived many perils, and knew the hearts of woodland things. He did not want to be caught by a furious ambush of bees from some hidden point on the trunk, or some secondary exit from the city, just when he was at work at the gates. But he found the trunk bare, except for a solitary tree grub, which he ate absent-mindedly.

Having reached the platform, he sat still, listening and watching. He looked exceedingly handsome, with his vivid grass-green back, scarlet crown and scarlet-splashed face, his strong bill and alert black eyes.

Having ascertained and recognized all the woodland sounds, and the sounds of the distant fields, and of children playing a mile away, and having scrutinized everything within sight, he suddenly uttered a piercing, yaffling laugh, and struck the oak, just above the bees' gateway, with his beak. He struck three times, with incredible swiftness, paused, struck once, paused, struck three times, paused . . . and so on for four or five turns; then stood motionless and expectant, watching the gateway.

Nothing happened. After a minute, he struck again, harder than ever, sending a tiny chip or two of bark flying, tapping, stopping, tapping, stopping, tapping again and again.

Then, again, he paused for a minute or two, and the wood which had rung with the sharp sounds seemed more still than ever.

Inside the city, the cluster was disturbed. Tiny vibrations from each tap shuddered through the oak, perceptible to the fine senses of the bees, and those outermost on the mass started to flex their legs and stir their wings. Then, suddenly, two of them dropped to the gateway and darted out furiously. They emerged one behind the other. Twice the woodpecker flicked his scarlet head—and they were swallowed down.

Once more that cackling laugh echoed obscenely through the avenues of stiff, bare trunks.

He stood still watching the gateway. He was very patient.

But no more bees emerged. So he began again, tap-tapping
sharply, flicking out the slivers of bark and wood, and then
pausing. This time he did not have to wait. Three more
bees came storming out together. Expertly and at incredible
speed he picked them off. Each was snapped and killed in
his bill before he swallowed the body. In all his life he had
never killed bees before; but yet he feared stings.

The game went on for an hour or more. About a dozen
bees were pecked up and swallowed. Now and then the
woodpecker screeched with laughter. Inside the oak, serious
disturbance was spreading all through the cluster. Feet and
antennae were moving restlessly. The outer part of the
cluster had grown bodily loose; hundreds of bees were preparing to drop, and to emerge with a sudden rush like that
of a Zulu impi at the charge. They knew their sentries had
vanished. There was no hum or murmur from outside, no
sign of them patrolling across the entrance; only that menacing tapping.

They did not, in the end, have to fight. The last bee the
woodpecker swallowed was as dead as the rest, broken into
bits by the snap of the merciless beak; but the sting, still
protruding from the tail, touched the side of the bird's inner throat in being swallowed. The barb caught, and a tiny
flicker of poison trickled into the flesh, all that would go
now that the bee's muscles could no longer squirt the stuff
along the dart.

It was enough. With a whirl of rage and fear, the woodpecker dropped to the base of the trunk and appeared to
bounce from there into another tree and from that one to
another and another, out of sight. He shook his vivid head,

beat his beak savagely on trees as he landed on them, and flapped his wings.

Very angry, terrified, but soon healed, he never approached that oak tree again. All his life he had been cautious, never needing a lesson twice. When he passed by, he stared at the tree malignantly out of fierce black eyes, opened his beak suddenly and emitted a shrill, sardonic laugh. Never again!

It was fortunate for the bees. Otherwise he might have gone there for every meal, perhaps for weeks. At the first sign of a mass eruption of bees he would have fled cackling into the wood, only to return when all was quiet again. The actual losses would not have been very high, but the cluster, disturbed and worried, would have eaten far too much, as always in excitement, and would have broken its solid defenses against the cold. Dysentery, too free flying, and disaster must then inevitably have followed.

Even as it was, there was a heavy consumption of food during the rest of that day and the ensuing night. All the honey cells within reach were emptied. Then, with a fresh closing down of the bitter cold, the bees were unable to stir from the tightened cluster.

Day followed day, and the cold grew more relentless. The bees dared not move. Those towards the outside grew cold and became apathetic. The gentle rhythm of their warming movements slowed—eventually stopped. The chill drew up round them like rising water. They struggled a little against it, but the effort was too great. The desire to rest, to be still, to sleep, overmastered them. One by one, and then score after score, sank into a torpor.

After a period of deathlike stillness, they began to move

blindly, forced reluctantly by gnawing hunger. They turned aimlessly and slowly about on the combs. They plunged their heads in agonies into empty cells, thrusting down so far, with a last maniacal strength, that their whole bodies were almost enclosed. And so died silently, hundreds of them, never having known a springtime.

There was still ample honey in other combs. All they had to do was to jump a few inches to reach a place where golden pounds of honey hung. They could not do it. Hibernation, that little death, now had them drugged in thick, poppy-colored mists. Their eyes looked round but conveyed no meanings from what they saw. The honey they could smell was one with the honey that had been gathered through the millions of years of all the earth's changing flowers. Though, later on, their legs continued to carry those at the base, on warmer days, up to the top of the cluster, they did not know where they were going or why, any more than sleepwalkers do. The bodies of them all quivered in the slow measure that preserved warmth in the cluster, but they did it, as they breathed, without conscious deliberation and without memory of having done it. Through the communal intelligence passed dim, confused pictures of the past—vague dreams of bees glorying among the fadeless flowers of Eden while man and maid who were all-good spoke to them, and of bees who nested at the feet of the Stone Men the Greeks worshiped, and of bees who established themselves under a rock facing Pan's altar in the oakwood, when Roman legionaries feasted with brown British girls, and the great goat-footed figure had not yet become only a sighing ghost.

And with the memories came increasing yearnings for

sights and smells and colors that pricked the opiate mists of hibernation with delicious pains. Already, imperceptibly, the days were lengthening, the cruel nights shortening. The bees were sleepier than ever; but they were feeling the birth throes of new life.

Among the clustering, dreaming bees, there was the first tingling of a new movement, not directed negatively merely to preventing cold, but throbbing and trembling outwards to greet something that was coming, something that every living thing quivers to know again, to which the flesh itself gives answer.

The springtime . . .

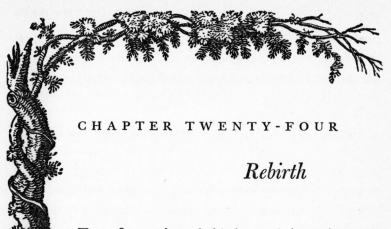

CHAPTER TWENTY-FOUR

Rebirth

THAT fierce winter held the earth in an iron grip until after January had ended. The ground was like rock, the living things dared hardly move.

Then there came softly in the night a warm wind from the south, and the sun rose majestically, dispersing frost and beating down on gray grass and black tree, and especially on the oak that sheltered the golden city.

For hour after hour, as the sun climbed to the zenith, the bees in the cluster basked in the new warmth. They made no effort, for a long time, to stir themselves; but about midday there passed a general stretching and stirring through the whole mass of them, such as had never happened since the cluster was formed.

At the same time, a faint, subdued humming began in the very center of the moving ball. This humming marked the beginning of an epoch. The queen was working her way across the cells on the face of the center comb.

Her maids began to groom her with frantic eagerness; and though the cluster remained formed, sufficient space within it was created by nearby bees arching themselves over this new activity. The queen was brushed and combed and petted. Then, simultaneously, the half-dozen maids crouched round her, eagerly offering honey from their tongues.

This was a ceremonial; all through the long winter she had been fed in the same way as everyone else, but this was once more the royal way.

She accepted all the honey, taking a special and considerable meal. As she concluded, her maids, one by one, abandoned their crouching attitude, and leapt joyously into nearby cells, cleaning and polishing them out. The queen looked mildly round within the tiny chamber they had made for her, roofed with that vault of curved bodies, and then, seeking a cell to her liking, deposited there the first egg of the new life cycle.

As she did so, the faint humming rose suddenly to a triumphant roar that vibrated the whole cluster, the whole city, and seemed to send living tremors through the great oak.

She moved very quietly along the cells, pausing happily for several minutes here and there. In the warmest midday hours of that day, a dozen eggs were laid. And the next day, more; and though, after that, the cold came back again and laying was suspended, all knew it was suspended only, and that it would commence again as soon as the sun shone.

The dark road of the winter had been traversed—the deadly corner turned. Far ahead, but with every day now diminishing the distance, the flowers were, and the heat of the sun, the green world and the azure sky. Life, beckoning.

With what excitement nurses were elected to care for the babies so soon to be. With what a furious flurry bees by the score leaped down and started sweeping out the dead bodies, the broken wax and purely imaginary dust! How joyous the midday rush out of doors, the pinging flights at tremendous speed, like aerial races, round and round the oak and up and up into the blue heights! How eagerly hundreds of bees began cleaning out cells ready for more eggs, cells in many cases so far from the warm center of the cluster that under no circumstances could they be used for weeks yet, or even months! How sternly older bees took their places at the gates, not enrolled as sentries yet, but ready to face enormous perils for the sake of the new life within! How athletically others whisked their shining wings; fanners would not be needed in their lifetime, not indeed till generations had passed into dust; but they were ready to fan, if the sun should forget himself and suddenly turn winter into summer.

During the winter, though their respect for the person of the queen had not lessened, they had been only vaguely aware of her presence. But now once more she took the awe of godhead. Life—she alone held the seeds of life; none here around her would see the summer, but she would, and the fruit of her body would populate and conquer this summer and all the summers of coming history.

A day or two of sunshine, a day or two of cloud and cold—and then, a fresh morning, with a newer, brighter, yet more living sunshine still.

The bees knew. They felt a spirit moving in their flesh, stirring it to some adventure whose form was unknown. This disturbance caused them to flock out through the gates, hundreds of them, and crawl and flow about the alighting platform. It lifted their wings on their backs, crouched their legs, beat their wings, wildly filling their tracheae with air, lifted them despite themselves into the sky, and sent them sailing eagerly and hungrily along the tops of the naked hedges.

What did they seek? They did not know. Why were they thus ungovernably excited? They had no reason to answer this. But their eyes glittered down over all the earth, seeking something which should explain itself.

A sudden whining whir as a bee dived like a falling stone . . . and then they all had seen the hazel blooms, like the crimson banners of Lilliput, flaming along the hedge. The bees fell on them, clutching them in fervid embraces, forcing their virginity, sipping and storing the exquisite clear honey, and humming thanks to God while setting all the autumn nuts.

Another cohort of the bees, a mile away over the village, was diving to and jumping on and embracing blazing yellow aconites, fair snowdrops, and almost swarming in the thick-set blossom of the little box trees. From all these, not only honey was being gathered, but the bees, as fast as they could move, were stuffing their pollen bags tight with baby food.

The world was shining bright and new. A fresh wind scudded across the hill, and in its train a magical sheen of green touched everything. The bees romped in that warm and living air, staggering home with monstrous loads of pollen and intoxicating tastes of new honey, fragrant as Aurora's breath. As they gamboled in the wind over the hillside, the larks above them trilled and beat their way towards Heaven as though nothing less would do.

At the city gates there was a prankish gaiety. Bees knocked

each other over, raced in to compare honeys, flung great
loads of pollen into cells within.

The nights were bitter cold, and the cluster had to be
re-formed; but the days were halcyon days of lovingness and
selflessness and happiness supreme. Each day grew longer,
each day grew warmer, each day it was possible that some
new honey-giving flower would be sighted, seized, adored,
loved, fertilized so that it, too, might be immortal, while
offering joyously all its sweetness in return.

Each day the nursery section of the center comb expanded
a little, the first eggs broke, and from inert things, became
moving, living things, and these grew and formed and
dumbly felt the need for wings, and so were sealed mysteriously in faith and love, and then emerged, perfect and
winged, eager with that special eagerness with which young
things reach out to meet the loveliness of life.

That was a day—that day when the first bee emerged!
How she was fussed and petted, brushed and loaded with
honeys; and how gay and clean she was, compared with the
hairless, ragged-winged veterans who had triumphed over
black winter. How proud they were because she gently put
them aside and began of her own accord to fondle and care
for the younger brood, so expertly against their clumsiness,
so surely that their old experience trembled before her
innocence.

And then another and another of her kind, and dozens
of them, and scores of them; so many, soon, that an infinite
sense of peace and rest crept through the tired bodies of
all those who had outlived the winter, for now they knew
that survival was in safer keeping than their own.

The winter—who cared for the winter then? When blind-

ing sheets of hail came rattling on the oak and thrashing
the hedge twigs that were still bare of leaves, the bees made
merry in their secure castle and boasted that sunshine always
followed hail. When the cold rain swished across the hillside, they declared that they could smell the first plum
blossom in the air. When iron frosts flung a mantle of white
everywhere, they stared out of their propolis window and
swore that never had frost crystals been such splendid shapes
before.

The frosts melted before the all-conquering sun. The
buds on hedges and trees grew big; at their tips, uncurling
layers disclosed shining green points. Edging the paths of
the cottages down in the village, honeyed crocuses blazed;
girls and boys who had been children romping through last
summer looked at one another, now, and blushed, and shyly
looked again.

The old bees, rear guard of a vanished year, watched contentedly the throng of active, eager newcomers from the
ever-spreading nursery combs. First to discover and reach
new flowers, first to race to meet new tasks, these inheritors
could not subdue their wild impatience for the summer that
could be sensed already, coming from far away.

The queen-goddess remained among them, loving and
pitiful and wise; but those who had so arduously toiled and
fought that she might bear the flame of life through the
darkness, shrank to a handful, to a score . . . to one.

Alone with her great memories among a swift, careless
generation with different thoughts, this last survivor com-
muned with none. She saw the hurried doings of a new
generation only dimly as a sort of moving fog between her

and the heroic pictures of the lost summer to which she belonged.

The death-tapping of the woodpecker in those days when all the world was softly mantled in white; that great battle of the Giants, one of whom still lay there below, for ever encased in shining resin, over which these new young bees raced irreverently, thinking no more of it than if it had been a knot of wood; the death dance of the splendid drones, creatures such as these youngsters had never seen and would never see; the wax-moths against which she tried to warn them, but they listened in uncomprehending politeness; the fierceness of the wasps.

Further back, too, not in her own memory but clear because belonging to her own summer, the children of chalk; the gray shadows of the great plague; the ecstasy of purple heather filling all the world with sweetness and perfume; the robber swarms of death; the mountainous attack of the badger in the twilight; the glory of the clover fields; the light and warmth of such an eternal summer as the world, surely, would never know again.

With these very eyes, it seemed to this old bee, she had seen the goddess going shyly to her divine wedding, seen the great swarm dance down the summer sky, seen the joy-flight of thousands of baby bees of a more godlike mold than now, and seen a world of apple blossom dancing so daintily in the sunlight that never had heart lifted and breath come fast as it did then. . . .

The thought of that forgotten orchard stirred her tired body. She went down slowly to the city gates, where sentries she did not recognize stared darkly at her as she passed out, and closed up significantly behind her to forbid re-entry. But she never saw that merciless movement.

She was winging steadily up the sunny sky towards the village, towards the orchard she had never seen. She flew slowly, but that only gave her more time to taste the fullness of the wonderful world, with the leaves uncurling, the buds opening, the sun growing hotter.

She sought something—a flower—a new honey more perfect than earthly honey had been or could ever be.

She grew very tired before she had gone more than a few hundred yards. Her wings would hardly carry her. But her eyes scrutinized every glimmer of color, every unrecognized shape, with a clarity and ease that she had never known before, even in the height of her youth and strength. It seemed that she could see beyond the horizon, almost, into fields ablaze with flowers of unknown hues.

As she looked nearer, a golden star appeared, hidden at the foot of the hedge that straggled from the oakwood down towards the village. Instantly, the bee recognized that this was what she had set out to seek. With infinite thankfulness, she glided down and alighted, swinging, on the dandelion bloom.

She stood there for a long while, watching the shining green of the hillside, where the lambs frolicked just as they had done a year ago in this same place. Those lambs were gone; yet the world was just the same. The dandelions that had spread along the hedgerow then were dead, but here was the first of others just the same. The bees who had romped in the sunny air of that springtime were dust now, fertilizing a new spring for ever just the same.

The last of the ghosts of the old year that had gone, this

bee was dying in the sunshine that quickened life eternal. She had found the very first dandelion of the year in flower, but could not carry the message back to the golden city; nor did that matter, since thousands of lusty inheritors were there to search for and find and profit from all the dandelions and all the other blossoms that would ensue.

Death was almost here in this field beneath the singing larks and the scented wind; but life would go on.

Life, that vain shadow in which bees and men disquiet themselves to heap up riches, not knowing who will gather them; life, begun in physical perfection, but consuming away as it were a moth fretting a garment; life, that had been before the mountains were brought forth or ever the earth was made; life, that would go on for ever without end.

The bee, its dying vision contracting, seemed to stand in the midst of a scented field of the cloth of gold, more lovely and enduring even than the golden city that had been and would be for such innumerable bee generations safely guarded within the oak. The bee sank down into that yellow, shining forest, content to rest, on the very edge, at last, of understanding that true life is not quickened, except it die.

Piercing sweet, the wind blew through the reeds by the river, and in that moment the old bee drooped, and forgot the fitful fever of life, and became one with the everlasting comfort of the woods and fields. At the same sound, the growing thousands of newborn in the golden city quivered in the full sunshine of rebirth.